USAF CLOSE AIR SUPPORT

USAF CLOSE AIR SUPPORT

RICHARD S. DRURY

Motorbooks International
Publishers & Wholesalers
Printed in Singapore

This USA edition published in 1991 by
Motorbooks International,
Publishers & Wholesalers, PO Box 2,
729 Prospect Avenue,
Osceola, WI 54020, USA.

© Richard Drury 1991
Published by Airlife Publishing Ltd.,
Shrewsbury, England, 1991.

Motorbooks International is a certified trademark,
registered with the United States Patent Office.

Printed and bound in Singapore
by Kyodo Printing Co (S'pore) Pte Ltd.

The information in this book is true and complete
to the best of our knowledge. All recommendations
are made without any guarantee on the part of the
author or publisher, who also disclaim any liability
incurred in connection with the use of this data or
specific details.

We recognize that some words, model names and
designations, for example, mentioned herein are
the property of the trademark holder. We use them
for identification purposes only. This is not an
official publication.

Library of Congress Cataloging-in-Publication Data
ISBN 0-87938-564-2

While the final analysis, impressions and
judgments reached in this book are strictly
my own, they were formed after dozens
of interviews, flights and a good deal of
research. Pilot specialists from each airplane
have reviewed the text and all generally
support the results.

The product is the outcome of my quest to
fly the Skyraider's follow-on USAF close-
air-support (CAS) types, to see them from
the pilot's perspective on actual training
missions and to see what has happened to
the CAS mission through the years. I hoped
to put the reader in the cockpit with the
views of the pilot. When this book was
started, there were but three aircraft types
involved, the A-37, the A-7 and the A-10. Then
came the F-16 with its dedicated CAS role
with the 138th Tactical Fighter Squadron
(TFS) at Syracuse, New York.

For historical and technical data, thanks in
particular to the Cessna Aircraft Company,
the General Dynamics Corporation, the
General Electric Company, the LTV Aerospace and Defense Company, USAF Systems
Command, Office of Public Affairs and
the Aeronautical Systems Division, Wright
Patterson AFB.

I set a formidable task for myself when
I undertook to fly and photograph these
aircraft. That it was accomplished is a tribute
to so many fine people who opened the doors
and made it possible. There were literally
hundreds of people along the way and I
sincerely thank them all. My very special
thanks to the following:

Lt Colonel John L. Bradley, III, Group
Commander, 110th Tactical Air Support
Group (TASG), Battle Creek ANG; who also
let me discover that five hours in an A-37 is a
long, hard sit.

Lt Colonel Noel Hanna, 110th TASG,
Deputy Commander for Operations; thanks
also for the wisdom, wit and a notebook full
of memorable quotes.

Captain Kevin 'Rock' Darroch; for all your
time and effort for the nerve to actually order
a pink drink with an umbrella on it in front of
a table of fighter pilots.

General Gordon Stump, Commander,
Michigan ANG; for the A-7 introduction, a
great ride across the Arizona Desert, and
review of the text.

Lt Colonel Dick Czarnota for the excellent
A-7 photo flight.

Major Dan Wilson for all the assistance
as well as that great four-ship from Rickenbacker.

Major Al Frierson for his review and
additions.

General Gordon Campbell, Wing Commander, 121st TFW; for providing a great
photo platform even under tactical mission
maneuvers.

Colonel Thomas J. Costello, New York State
ANG Deputy Commander for Operations;
not only for setting up my F-16 experience
but for showing me how to drink beer
through my nose while inverted over the
pilot's bar.

Lt Colonel Phil Hofmann, Operations
Officer, 138th TFS; for the great F-16 flight
and review of the text with constructive
comments. Now, I want my own F-16!

To you all, if you have to do it, go fast and
may you only have one pass!

Opposite: Callsign Macho 11, Serial Number
73-087, an A-37B from the Battle Creek Air
National Guard pulls up from a low-level
pass at the Grayling air-to-ground range
(R4201) in the northern peninsula of
Michigan. Piloted by Lt Colonel Dave
Strohm, the training strike mission operates
in reduced visibility due to snow showers.
Station L4 has a B-37K-1 rack LAU-68 A/A
2.75 inch rocket launcher, a typical
peacetime training configuration.

USAF CLOSE AIR SUPPORT

Twenty years ago I flew my last close-air-support (CAS) mission in what had been the best CAS airplane of the time, the venerable Douglas A-1 Skyraider. In the early environment of the Southeast Asian war, the Skyraider had the right virtues: extensive loiter time, heavy and varied ordnance load, great accuracy and the ability to take hits and keep flying. We could virtually hold overhead the troops-in-contact (TIC) and stay with the action for hours. Ours was the last piston-engine combat aircraft manufactured in the USA and Douglas made over 3,000 of them ending in February of 1957. It fought from the beginning to the end of the Southeast Asian war and was there on April 30, 1975 when Saigon was evacuated.

We flew the Skyraider with panache, knowing we were the last of a breed, men who inhaled the fragrance of hot engine oil and worn leather, revelled in the rhapsody of the big radial engine, and could even tame a big taildragger. We were smug with the knowledge gained from direct observation that the jets could not do our CAS jobs with anywhere near the accuracy and endurance of our 'antiques'. Jets had an on-station time measured in minutes while ours was in hours. For whatever reasons they could not seem to hit targets with real accuracy while we were low and slow, 'in the weeds', and could put all manner of ordnance spot on. We took hits and kept on flying. Jets were fragile. And if we were still back in those halcyon days of low-intensity conflict the A-1 would still be among the best CAS airplanes, performing in the highly visible, over the target, manner the Army still wishes could be done. Unfortunately, a portent of things to come was the introduction of highly effective AAA which eventually received radar guidance. Except for search-and-rescue (SAR)

operations, we were relegated to night operations in such high-threat domains. Finally, with the introduction of the hand-held SAM, our swashbuckling era was over.

The CAS operation, by definition, involves the historic encounter of troops in contact, seen over the trenches of World War I, over Spain as Adolf Galland wrote more of the book in his He-51s with the Condor Legion, and later through pilots' gunsights over Korea, Vietnam and Laos. The current elaborate definition of CAS is: 'Air action against hostile targets in close proximity to friendly forces and which require detailed integration of each mission with the fire and movement of these forces.' Simply put, the CAS pilot must put ordnance on targets which are virtually next to the friendlies. The traditional mission objective remains much the same but the environment has changed dramatically. Anti-aircraft weapons are better, mobile, radar guided and the hand-held missile is a fact of life. The CAS pilot is asked to do much the same job but his tools and methods have to change.

The Army is the final customer for CAS operations and its doctrines have been modified. In 1982 the US Army introduced what is known as the Air–Land Battle precept, an overall view of how the Army and Air Force would operate together to fight future wars. The conventional CAS role is included but the aircraft are also asked to assume more of a role in what is known as battlefield interdiction (BAI), attacking the enemy forces before the situation becomes one of troops in contact. The technical BAI definition is: 'Air interdiction attacks against land force targets which have a near-term effect on the operations or scheme of maneuver of friendly forces, but are not in close proximity to friendly forces.' While CAS and BAI are

different missions, it can be seen that aircraft requirements are merging.

With few exceptions, the CAS pilot will now operate in an extremely high-threat arena. Even the most primitive and remote regions can rapidy become high-threat with hand-held missiles and mobile, radar-controlled weapons. Manpack weapons can now be employed wherever the troops are deployed. The Afghanistan conflict made this point brutally obvious. In the late 1980s, Stinger anti-aircraft missiles came into the Afghan guerrillas' possession. Russia's free reign of the skies ended abruptly. US Army findings indicate that the shootdown rate was almost 80 per cent. Errors and mechanical problems included, the Afghans terminated 269 of 340 Russian aircraft targeted. After a month's suspension of all flights, Russian pilots came back with low-level tactics which brought them not only into range of small arms fire as well as the missiles but introduced them to the accident prone nature of low-level operations where pilot tasks increase quickly. While the Russians had a host of countermeasures from flares to infra-red jammers they ended up in mostly night missions to avoid the hand-held missiles. Clearly, most any enemy ground force can tote a thirty pound anti-aircraft missile weapon and most any army of even the most meager country will have them. While the low-level operation is generally recognized as standard procedure in these high-threat areas, the hazards, as mentioned, are many. In the attempt to thwart radar's eye, the pilot goes low. AAA/SAM radar gets a better picture when the airplane is high and has more time to lock on. The lower the pilot operates the less time the weapons operator has to acquire the target. He can have minutes if the airplane is above 500 feet above ground level (AGL) but that time is reduced to seconds if the aircraft is at 100 feet AGL, is going fast, and using terrain masking. Adding the pilot's countermeasures, very low flying affords survivability unavailable elsewhere. But it is extremely dangerous. Not only is the pilot hoping to avoid SAMs, AAA, and small-arms fire, he is also hoping to avoid hitting the terrain. In low visibility operations (the war goes on regardless of the weather) the CAS pilot has a formidable job!

As the Gulf War has illustrated, the high-altitude environment becomes more viable as ECM improves because pilots can over-fly most AAA and IR SAMs. However, high-technology equipment and reliable performance is critical — particularly with an air-threat.

There are those who suggest that a slower aircraft, able to locate and stay with a target, able to take hits and deliver great firepower, is the answer. At the other end of the spectrum is the conviction that survivability will be a matter of low-altitude, high-speed operation, where the one-pass attack is all that might be feasible. Thus, the position that aircraft speed and agility is essential.

Certainly, when the pilot operates in such close proximity to friendly forces, extreme accuracy is imperative. Electronic navigation and supremely accurate weapons deployment is the order of the day. The classic picture of a Forward Air Controller (FAC) orbiting the target and relaying location and target information is probably no longer realistic. There is little doubt that the historically customary airborne FAC cannot survive in the high-threat area. Most of us who flew the battles of Korea, Vietnam or Laos conjure the image of checking in with the FAC, being briefed on the target, possibly with respect to a marker or ground reference point, giving the FAC the ordnance lineup, making the attack, getting bomb damage assessment (BDA) and heading on home. Not only is it no longer reasonable to assume the FAC can survive the defenses, but jamming may well negate any typical FAC voice communication process.

While the Gulf War was truly an anomaly in what is perceived as the face of modern warfare, it does show that any such conclusions depend on how successful the defense suppression campaign has been. In fact, the best FAC in Operation Desert Storm may well have been the Lockheed U-2/TR-1 flying at over 70,000 feet and providing real-time battlefield data.

Target acquisition will be onerous. The 'mudfighter' proponents say that only a slow aircraft, maneuverable, with the ability to sustain damage, can get close, locate the target, identify it, then attack. Of course, the enemy now has more time to fire on the aircraft. Thus the slow-movers have adopted a number of evasions tactics that the fast movers employ. So, the other side asks, if they are adopting systems and operations that work for the fast-movers, why go slow at all? With installation of new systems such as automatic target handoff system (ATHS), speed will become less of a discriminator for target acquisition success than it has been in the past. There will seldom be a need to spend time trying to find the target, the old fast jet nemesis. Any pilot who has worked with the FAC system knows that a great deal of time is consumed in making contact, in getting a precise determination of the target, of transferring ordnance information, safe areas for bailout, defenses and whatever else may be pertinent. Voiceless, the ATHS simply transfers all the relevant target information from the observer, whether on the ground or in the air, to a print-out on the pilot's head-up display (HUD). Well away from the target, the pilot now has all target information which he inserts in his computer. With the increase in target hand-off accuracy and speed, the fast-movers may become the most effective solution for CAS in the high-threat region. The notion that fast jets cannot perform the CAS function due to speed and lack of accuracy just does not ring true with modern navigation and weapons delivery systems.

Whether the operation is coverage of a deeply inserted friendly force or BAI, another aspect of the equation emerges: the aircraft may have to penetrate enemy territory for some distance, not just overfly the friendlies to the TIC location. Aircraft requirements are merging. A BAI aircraft for one mission may be CAS for the next. Some missions, such as the deeply inserted friendly force, have elements of both CAS and BAI. Further, CAS/BAI aircraft must now face the reality of intercept by hostile aircraft, particularly on any deep penetration of hostile territory. The ability to compete successfully in such situations may be a requirement to enter, support TIC, and exit the battle area. There is obviously the hope that fighter air-cover would be provided for the CAS/BAI mission but CAS typically can become a spur-of-the-moment surprise situation and adequate fighter assets may not be immediately available. The CAS pilot may well be on his own with perhaps only mutual support from his wingman or others in his flight. In an encounter with enemy fighters, the CAS pilot can have the dubious option of continuing an attempt to support ground troops and dying with his machine, or maybe even becoming the subject of a search and rescue in the midst of the initial ground force encounter or, if he has an air combat maneuvering (ACM) capable aircraft, engaging and hopefully eliminating the threat. Either way, the Army will not like it, but it seems absurd to pretend that days of old are back and demand continuous overhead protection of the troops when the mission may not even be viable.

Considering the continuing sophistication of enemy reaction to air attack, the CAS pilot now may be faced with a one pass attack. If surprise is achieved, the pilot stands the best opportunity to make his attack and survive. However, on later passes the situation will be different. Now the shoulder-fired SAMs will be ready, vehicular-mounted guns will have been unlocked and pointed, the SAM mobile and ZSUs will have stopped, and the missile and gun crews will be searching the sky. Research and tests indicate that the reduction of the number of passes is the most significant survivability parameter. Thus navigational accuracy, precise target acquisition and accuracy of weapons delivery are paramount.

A typical problem is encountered when we try to make one airplane all things to everyone. But in this era of deep budget cuts and the fashionable thought that there is now a peace-loving Russia, there will be no funding for a true, modern CAS airplane. The way politicians and bureaucrats work, a new close-air-support airplane would take ten to twelve years to get and cost billions of dollars. That option was discarded. What will emerge is a version of a current aircraft. Of course, there is also the option of providing two types of aircraft, one for the high-threat areas and one for low-intensity combat, a mix of A-10s and F-16s, for example. If the troops and tanks are isolated, removed from AAA capability and air interception, the slow-mover, like the A-10, could do what it was designed to do. And that result is precisely what we saw in the A-10's engagement with Iraqi troops and equipment. Otherwise, the F-16s would do their electronic one pass maneuver.

There is also serious thought that the CAS mission is no longer viable, that no matter what the aircraft, it cannot enter future CAS engagements in the typical high-threat world of combat and survive. While the Army and other 'mudfighter' advocates may enjoy the vision of the heavily armed beast circling overhead, attacking the hostile troops and saving the day, such dreams may be no more than wishful thinking. Certainly, there are also those who feel that the US should never have to commit large ground armies as we have in the past, that if we did then we have wasted all our technology and advanced weapons. But wars are not won by shooting down an airplane or destroying a tank. The ground force is required to advance and occupy.

Further, drawing long-term, valid conclusions from the Gulf War is extremely difficult — and in many cases, probably a mistake. In the assessment of aircraft capabilities in the glow of the "victory," one must wonder just how much credit should be given to an enemy air force that ran away, a navy that was virtually non-existent, an army sans military reconnaissance or intelligence, and an awesome military force provided by numerous countries.

As we pointed out, one thing is certain: the future holds less funding for military systems, not more. The desire and ability to construct a new CAS aircraft is virtually gone. New, private, ventures offering 'cheap' CAS alternatives beg the question. Without ACM capability, modern electronic datalink, and ECM, at the very least, these designs become a moot point.

The USAF and its Reserve and National Guard components is generally charged with overall CAS responsibility for the Army and has committed the A-37, A-7 and specifically the A-10 to that role. With an eye towards future battlefields, the F-16 has been introduced. Since the Air Force is the prime CAS provider for the Army, it is the focus of this book.

The author's observations and comments may heat up the debate even more but I have listened to those who have flown each of the CAS types and who have flown combat missions in them. I have had the good fortune to talk with pilots who have personally flown ALL the types and I have used their input and vision in my analysis. Unfortunately, the outcome and final product will be political, obviously no guarantee of quality, excellence or capability.

CESSNA A-37 DRAGONFLY

In December of 1952 Cessna Aircraft Company's Model 318 was judged the winner of a USAF design competition for an economical jet trainer. The aircraft was given the Air Force designation of T-37 and the first prototype, the XT-37, flew on October 12, 1954.

The introduction of the aircraft to USAF student pilots was delayed by a number of modifications including cockpit alterations, wing center-section strengthening, changes to the J-69 engine's fuel system and modifications to deal with poor nose wheel steering, inadequate brakes, undesirable stall and spin characteristics as well as a very high-pitched engine whine. All of the problems were solved except the loud whistle which stayed with the T-37 trainer, earning it a number of sobriquets including 'Tweet', 'the 6,000 pound dog whistle' or 'the airplane that converts jet fuel into noise — only'.

The US Army tested three T-37As (#56-3463, 3465 and 3466) in a ground support role in 1957. Thereafter, possibly influenced by the Army's tests, the USAF saw a need for a light attack aircraft for CAS missions, then known as 'Counterinsurgency' or COIN operations. The A-37 was derived to meet that need.

In 1962 Cessna converted two T-37Bs to the COIN role for USAF evaluation. In the armed role they were underpowered and so converted to two General Electric J85-GE-5 engines of 2,400 pounds thrust. Redesignated the YAT-37D in October of 1963, their performance was vastly improved. The aircraft were also configured with tip tanks and a stronger wing with six weapon pylons.

In 1966 Cessna was contracted to modify thirty-nine T-37Bs into the A-37A. J85-GE-17A engines derated to 2,400 pounds thrust were installed and Cessna delivered the first

A-37A in May of 1967. The USAF had a simple design, low cost, low maintenance COIN aircraft with maneuverability and the reliability of two engines.

Further modifications included larger gear struts, wheels, tires and brakes. Provision was also made for a GAU-2B/A 7.62mm minigun in the nose. The electrical system was upgraded to accommodate CAS mission ordnance and armor-plating was added along with shatterproof glass.

During 1967 twenty-five A-37As were sent to Vietnam for a four month evaluation. The 604th Special Operations Squadron carried out the mission under the name 'Combat Dragon'. The unit was based at Bien Hoa and Pleiku, and the first combat mission was flown in August of 1967. The A-37 was evaluated on its ability to perform the CAS mission, helicopter escort, armed reconnaissance, FAC operations as well as night interdiction. Two different color schemes were used in the tests: the conventional Southeast Asia camouflage of medium green (FS 34102), dark green (FS 34079), and dark tan (FS 30219) over a bottomside color of camouflage gray (FS 36622), and an experimental light blue-gray top color with the flat gray undersides. The tests were generally successful and no aircraft were lost. During this period it was suggested that the aircraft be given the name 'Dragonfly', although the name 'Super Tweet' was more commonly used. Several shortcomings in the aircraft were noted and modifications resulted in the A-37B, the final version of the aircraft.

As a combat aircraft in the modern CAS setting, the A-37's faults emerge. With a side-by-side seating configuration, cross-cockpit

visibility to the pilot's right is severely hampered. Cockpit layout is archaic by today's standards which forces the pilot to go into the cockpit, 'heads-down', to make virtually any selection of armament, radio frequency change or system management. The cockpit is noisy, fatiguing, unpressurized and cramped, particularly with two people aboard or a fuel tank in the right seat position. Fuel burn is high and the airplane suffers from limited range. There is virtually no air-to-air capability although the A-37B *Aircrew Weapons Delivery Manual* does discuss the potential of 'air attack' with the 7.62mm minigun, probably an unlikely event, particularly since the aircraft should close to a range of 2,000 feet or less due to the limited effective range of the gun. There is no ECM, no radar, no chaff or flares to counter missiles and fighter attack would most likely be lethal. There will be no US funding for this aircraft so all modern electronic upgrades will escape the A-37. Thus, the airplane will still rely on visual target acquisition, voice communication with a FAC or observer and manual weapons delivery techniques.

While the A-37 still maintains a CAS mission, it is easily seen that it would only be effective in a basic, permissive combat environment, a luxury perhaps never to be experienced again.

The aircraft is the subject of foreign military sales to so-called 'third world' nations, particularly those of Central and South America. For example, Columbia, Peru, Honduras and El Salvador operate the aircraft and are acquiring more. The Battle Creek ANG unit has even delivered them. Unfortunately, even those locations can have upgraded AAA and hand-held SAMs overnight. The A-37 and other 'trainer-to-attack' or hybrid private venture CAS entrants, technically and aerodynamically primitive, stand a quick demise in such an arena. Their best hope is to arrive at the onset of hostilities and use the element of surprise for a one-time attack. Longevity will rapidly decrease as the conflict matures.

The upgraded A-37B featured increased engine thrust (2,850 pounds per engine), an inflight refuelling system, increased fuel capacity, and an airframe stressed to six 'Gs'. Deliveries of the 'B' model began in 1968.

The A-37B was considered to be a replacement for the Vietnamese Air Force (VNAF) Douglas A-1 Skyraiders. Some sixty A-37Bs went to the VNAF's 524th Fighter Squadron in 1968. In May of 1969, fifty-four A-37Bs were assigned to the 524th, 520th, and 516th Fighter Squadrons. The A-37 staffed ten VNAF squadrons, finally replacing the A-1 as the main VNF fighter-bomber, CAS aircraft. It also became the prevailing VNAF combat aircraft. It enjoyed great success due to its simplicity, agility, and low maintenance and operational demands. It was combat effective until advanced AAA and SAMs brought a new face to the CAS environment.

During the closing hours of the Vietnam War a number of aircraft escaped from South Vietnam including twenty-seven A-37s to U Tapao, Thailand. It is estimated there are ninety-five A-37s left in Vietnam. It is also interesting to note that on April 28, 1975, three A-37s bombed Tan Son Nhut Air Base, ostensibly piloted by former VNAF pilots forced into enemy service, most likely the last actual combat action by the A-37.

In regular USAF service, the A-37 served with eleven units, although only the 604th SOS was to fly the 'A' model in combat. All others were equipped with the 'B' model. Following the end of United States involvement in Southeast Asia, the A-37B served operationally only in Korea, all others being withdrawn from regular service and flown in Reserve and Air National Guard squadrons. All remaining A-37s of the Air National Guard have been equipped for the FAC mission although they maintain their CAS capability and train for that mission as well.

Currently, the only active duty A-37 unit is in Panama serving with the Southern Command and only two active A-37 squadrons remain in Air National Guard service at Battle Creek, Michigan and Peoria, Illinois for a total of less than sixty US-flown A-37s. At this writing, the Battle Creek unit is destined to transition to the OA-10, and the Peoria unit is scheduled to receive F-16As.

An A-37 of the 110th Tactical Air Support Group begins its taxi from the Battle Creek flightline on a bitter Michigan morning. With cold temperatures, the muscle of two J85 engines in the small aircraft delivers a lot of obvious punch.

ANALYSIS

The A-37 is an old CAS airplane, its vintage comparable to that of the last Douglas A-1 Skyraider it was to replace in VNAF service. In a fairly permissive combat environment such as the early years of the Southeast Asian war, it has unique assets. It is a very small aircraft and is thus very difficult to see. At low altitudes with terrain masking, it is hard to locate visually. With an excellent thrust-to-weight ratio it is agile, accelerates well, and is easy to fly. Unlike later 'high-tech' aircraft, the A-37 is the sort of airplane that makes few demands of its pilot. Indeed, many pilots have said that the A-37 is the sort of airplane one can be away from for a long period, come back, and not burn yourself. Aircraft systems are basic and simple, which, coupled with its diminutive size, allows a short turnaround time for fuel and maintenance and thus can support multiple daily missions. The airplane sits so low that even ladders are eliminated. The pilot basically steps into the cockpit. It has a safety advantage of two engines which are smokeless, helping to hide it from visual acquistion. It is rugged, has very high maintenance reliability, and supports a 7.62mm minigun. It carries a respectable CAS ordnance load, typically two 750 pound Mk-117 bombs and two 500 pound Mk-82 bombs, plus two 250 pound Mk-81 bombs with no external fuel and 1,500 rounds of 7.672mm strafe. The aircraft is capable of delivering a variety of other ordnance including cluster bomb units (CBU) and rockets.

Top right: Three A-37s sit in the 'last chance' area before takeoff. Near the runway's end, ground crews perform final visual checks looking for such items as leaks, open covers, unsecured latches and safe ordnance.

Bottom right: In the 'last chance' position, this Battle Creek ANG pilot completes his checklist just before a dawn takeoff as snow showers sweep across the field.

Opposite: Wyatt flight, five A37s from Battle Creek, Michigan, pose line abreast *en route* to the annual 'Snowbird' event at Davis Monthan AFB, where units from all over the USA are able to perform tactical training in generally excellent weather. In this case, there is a 1,340 NM cross-country and three air refuellings involved for Battle Creek's 110th TASG. Cruise, here at FL 220, is about 240 knots indicated airspeed at 93 per cent power and a total fuel flow of 2,200 pounds per hour.

Top right: Forty minutes after takeoff from Battle Creek, the first A-37 'Wyatt 81', about to make contact with 'Backy 77', a KC-10 tanker from the Air Force Reserve unit at Seymour Johnson AFB, North Carolina. At a gross weight of over 400,000 pounds, this KC-10's body angle will be very high, obvious here at 235 knots.

Bottom right: The A-37's diminutive size is evident compared to the KC-10. The drogue refuelling system is required on the A-37 as it is not equipped to receive a boom probe. Total JP-4 fuel capacity is 5,503.5 pounds.

Opposite: Receiving fuel from the KC-10 at FL 210, the A-37 is hard-pressed to maintain contact at 235 knots while the heavy KC-10 is slow, nose high. Fuel transfer rate to the A-37 is from 500 to 1,000 pounds per minute (PPM), generally about 700 PPM. Air refuelling permits all internal and external tanks (except a right seat tank) to be filled inflight.

Above: Parked on the Davis Monthan AFB North Ramp, this A-37B displays four 100 gallon fuel tanks on stations L1, L2, R1 and R2. Stations L3 and R3 are empty. Station L4 has a B-37K-1 rack to hold four BDU-33 practice bombs and station R4 has a LAU-68 A/A rocket launcher. Each wingtip has a 90 gallon fuel tank installed. The A-37 flaunts a profusion of antennas, noticeable is the VHF-FM whip behind the canopy followed by a TACAN, UHF radio blade and the vertical FM homing antennas attached to the horizontal stabilizer's leading edge. Easy access to the fuel tank filler caps is clearly shown. Empty weight of the A-37 is 6,254 pounds. Wingspan with tip tanks is 38.34 feet and height is only 9.47 feet.

Opposite: Prominent on the A-37B's nose is the aerial refuelling nozzle leading to the distinctive refuelling manifold through which fuel flows to all of the fuel tanks. Also shown on the nose is the blast tube for the 7.62mm MAU-58 A/A nose gun. All paint on the top coat is MIL-C-83286 polyurethane of the Federal Standard (FS) 595A specification. The paint scheme is known as 'Euro One', a combination of FS 36081 — 'Euro One Gray', FS 34079 — 'Dark Green', FS 37038 — 'Flat Black' (for lettering purposes), and FS 17875 — 'Insignia White'.

Above: The technologically primitive, 'round-dial' instrument panel illustrates the A-37's vintage. Atop the pilot's panel is the CA-511 non-computing fixed reticle gunsight and directly below is the armament panel. The main flight instruments are in front of the pilot with two vertical rows of engine instruments in the center. Continuing across is the fuel control panel, two vertical rows of annunciator lights, then flight instruments for a right seat pilot or observer. Circuit breaker panels are prominent on the right cockpit sidewall.

Opposite: The right nose section contains the A-37's MAU-58 A/A nose minigun system, a 7.62mm air-cooled, self-charging, self-clearing, electrically-driven weapon. A nose gun rate switch on the instrument panel selects the firing rate with 'High' and 'Low' settings. At 'High', the nose gun fires at 5,500 to 7,000 rounds per minute with a muzzle velocity of 2,750 feet per second. The gun provides 15 seconds of continuous fire at the 'High' setting. The gun's empty weight is 157 pounds and 235 pounds loaded. The assembled gun length is 33.6 inches and total capacity is 1,500 rounds. Spent shell cases are ejected into a container located under the gun.

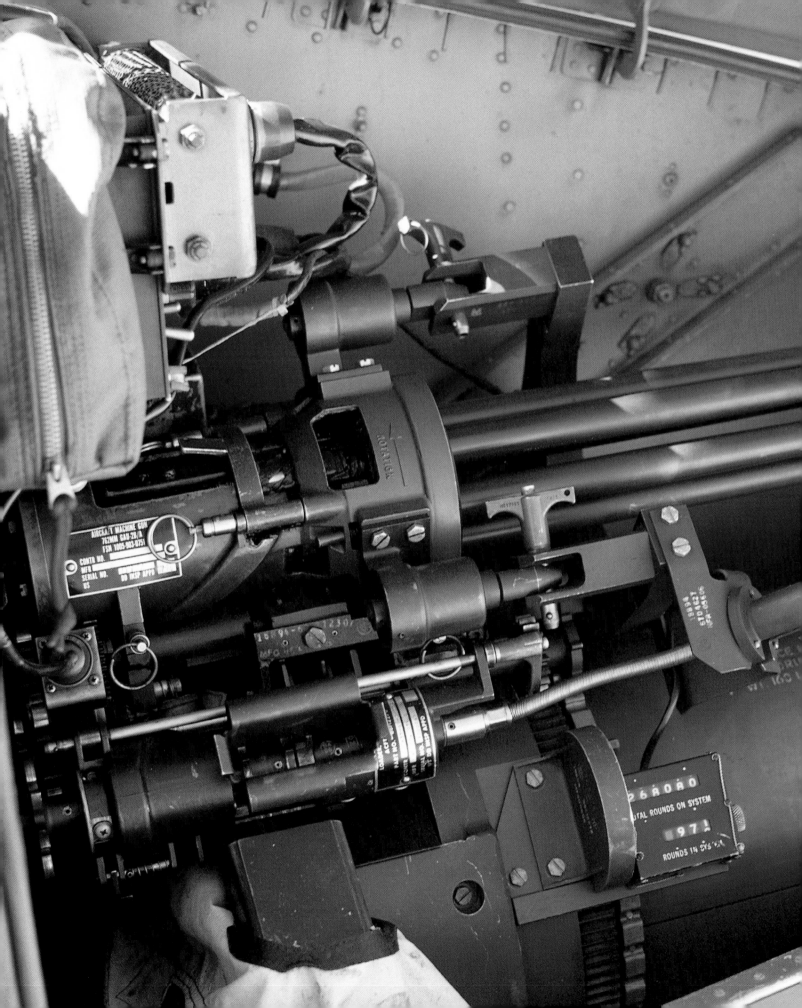

Above: The retracted (open) starboard thrust attenuator is seen in this starboard aft view. The function of the thrust attenuator is to reduce effective thrust and still maintain a higher engine RPM. The attenuators are used primarily for approach and landing but may be used on the ground to slow taxi speed. When actuated, they extend out to block the engine's thrust. Also evident is the faded and worn appearance of the flat paint.

Opposite: A port side, trailing edge view showing the tail area of two 100 gallon pylon fuel tanks. The wing fillets contain an access cover to the oil tank which holds four quarts in each system. A transducer vane located on the left nacelle is electronically connected to stall warning spoilers. With flaps down approximately 25 per cent and a critical angle-of-attack is approached, the vane activates the hydraulically operated spoilers to the 'out' position to provide sufficient stall warning for flap down configurations. The triangular scoop on top of the engine cowling is an air intake for cooling air around the hot section of the engine. The 'gills' are located just above the engine bleed valves. The engine bleed valves are usually open at low RPM (during engine start) and these gills provide a vent for that air.

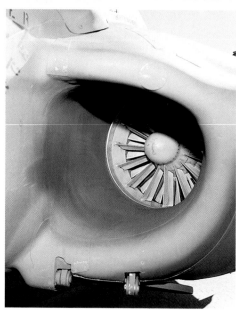

Above: Port side view of the engine inlet leading to the port General Electric J85-17A axial flow, turbojet engine. Approximate standard sea level maximum thrust rating is 2,850 pounds per engine. Two hinges are located on each inlet lip bottom and are attached to a retractable air inlet screen. Seen here, the screen is stowed under the lower front edge of the nacelle. When extending, the screens rotate around the lower tips of the intake and cover the inlet to prevent ingestion of foreign objects on the ground or inflight.

Above: At the 'Snowbird' event, Davis Monthan AFB, Arizona, Lt Colonel Kencil Heaton, 172 TASS Commander, briefs a low-level ingress route to the north tactical range in the Goldwater Range Complex in Arizona. The red circles are noise sensitive areas and are briefed as ground threat areas such as AAA or SAM sites. The red lines are the MOA (Military Operating Area) boundaries. Lt Colonel Heaton flew the A-37 with the 604th Special Operations Squadron and the 8th Special Operations Squadron at Bien Hoa Air Base, Republic of Vietnam, from June of 1970 to February of 1971.

Right: The A-37 1,000 hour patch is fairly rare since the actual airplane is now scarce. In Southeast Asian operations, an A-37 pilot might have logged from 300 to 400 hours during his combat tour. In ANG/reserve operations, a full-time ('technician') pilot could possibly obtain 1,000 hours in a four or five year period. Most other pilots could expect that much time in perhaps seven years. This patch is worn by Lt Colonel Heaton of the Battle Creek ANG unit.

Above: A-37B, serial number 73-059 on departure from Davis Monthan AFB, Arizona *en route* to the tactical range. BDU-33 blue practice bombs are seen on the left wing station. Note how the air loads bend all the whip antennas.

Right: An A-37 circles within the confines of the New Cornelia Ajo Copper Mine *en route* to the tactical range in the Goldwater complex between Tucson and Gila Bend, Arizona. the A-37's agility and tight turn radius made this spectacular photo possible.

Above: Aboard OA-37B, serial number 701-312, callsign 'Snow 54', at the tactical air-to-ground desert range in Arizona. The impact of marking rockets can be seen off the nose indicating the target area for a flight of A-37Bs on a strike/CAS training mission. Marking rockets used today are 2.75 inch folding fin aircraft rockets (FFAR), white phosphorus ('Willie Pete' or 'WP'), MK-66 rockets. Gas pressure from the rocket motor opens the rocket's folding finds which are shaped aluminum alloy plates 6.5 inches long by 1.26 inches wide. When folded they extend to the rear within the 2.75 inch diameter of the round. White phosphorus is a wax-like substance that melts at 111 degrees F. The most characteristic property of WP is spontaneous ignition when exposed to air, burning with a yellow flame producing a large volume of white smoke. Normal marking distance is approximately one mile but in a high-threat environment a rocket can be fired from over five miles, although accuracy suffers when lofting a rocket that distance.

Opposite: An A-37 pulling off a CAS pass, the target marked by the 2.75 inch smoke rockets of an OA-37B FAC. The A-37 is visually difficult to acquire owing to its small size and smokeless engine advantage, although the Euro One paint scheme does not help against the backdrop of a barren tan desert landscape.

A 110th TASG A-37B in its cross-country configuration loaded to carry fuel for the rapid consumption of the twin J85 engines. The A-37 marks the end of another era in close-air-support aviation for the United States. Along with its propeller counterpart, the Douglas A-1 Skyraider, it fought valiantly in Southeast Asia but found its days numbered by advanced anti-aircraft weaponry and late aeronautical technology.

LTV A-7 CORSAIR II

As the United States Navy revels in pointing out, following the F-4 Phantom and the Douglas A-1 Skyraider, the A-7 is yet another great Naval aircraft to be purchased by the Air Force. Actually, sailors can also gloat over the fact that it was also the Navy which first recognized the requirement for a specialized attack 'A' aircraft classification. Following World War II, it became obvious to Naval planners that in addition to fighters and bombers a new category was needed, one designed solely for the air-to-ground mission. Thus, the Navy advanced the 'A' for Attack aircraft classification which would become comprised of both large and small attack aircraft. The Douglas AD/A-1 Skyraider and A-4 Skyhawk comprised the initial, lighter, tactical attack aircraft of this new classification. It might be noted that while the Skyraider fell into this classification, it was certainly no slouch in terms of load-carrying capability as it routinely carried its own weight and that of a B-17 at around 12,500 pounds of external ordnance!

In the early 1960s the Navy elected to look for a replacement for these attack aircraft, hoping to secure increased ordnance delivery capability, range, and advanced performance. Pressed by the acceleration of the Southeast Asian war, the Navy also decided that time was of the essence and the complex and lengthy process of conception, design, test and production for an entirely new aircraft was out of the question and that is what the initial heavier-than-air, attack, experimental (VAX) program would have generated.

A shift was made to a heavier-than-air, attack, light (VAL) or light attack aircraft program which would be based upon existing designs of which four were examined. These were the Vought F-8 Crusader, the Grumman A-6 Intruder, the North American FJ Fury, and the Douglas A-4 Skyhawk. Design parameters also mandated a slower, subsonic aircraft which appeared to be diametrically opposed to the concept that ever-increasing speed and performance was desirable. Of course, in the early 1960s to locate a target and strike with accuracy, the philosophy was advanced that speed was no advantage, actually it could hinder the attack, and ordnance delivery with any accuracy was more of a slow-speed operation. The Navy also advanced the notion that sans high-speed technology, the slower airplane would be less expensive to produce. Here is the genesis of the low-and-slow is best and cheapest concept that pervades views nearly thirty years later.

On February 11, 1964 it was announced that the Vought concept had won the design competition. the Secretary of the Navy heralded the aircraft as the first designed for CAS and attack since World War II. By this time, Chance Milton Vought's company had been merged with James Ling's Ling-Temco Corporation in 1961. The new company was known as Ling-Temco-Vought, or LTV, which finally became known as the LTV Aerospace and Defense Corporation.

The full-scale mockup of the proposed aircraft was unveiled on June 25, 1964, and the company's Model V-463 took the next number in the USN attack lineup as the A-7A.

While the new aircraft was derived from the F-8 and had certain visual similarities to the original Crusader, the A-7 was essentially a new airplane and was named the 'Corsair II', a tribute of sorts to the original Vought, propeller-driven F4U Corsair which saw intensive combat in World War II and Korea. The F4U Corsair is venerated and known for its distinctive inverted gull-wing shape as well as its former combat capabilities.

The A-7's wing was fixed, in contrast to the F-8's variable-incidence wing, and a more efficient flap system was incorporated to provide higher lift. The thirty-five degree sweepback feature was retained. The airfoil section selected was an NACA 64A007 profile with built-in camber of the leading edge and had negative dihedral (anhedral) of five degrees. The high-wing configuration of the F-8 was also retained, which meant easier access underneath for both maintenance and weapons loading. A combination of inboard spoilers and outboard ailerons provided roll control with a backup feature that, should loss of ailerons occur, lateral control could still be maintained by the spoilers as well as slot deflectors underneath the flap leading edges, the spoiler-deflectors improving the rolling movement provided by the conventional ailerons.

Considerable thought was given to damage control aspects of the design. The wing structure was constructed as a fail-safe multi-cell box with spanwise spars and heavy skins. Should structural damage occur, torsion, shear and bending loads would be distributed to the intact cells. Finally, wing carriage of external weapons was provided by six wing pylons.

The fuselage was fairly conventional and, through the use of redistribution bulkheads, multiple, continuous longerons and frame stiffened shear-load carrying skins, provided another fail-safe structure. A number of quick access panels were installed in the lower fuselage area allowing rapid maintenance entry. A single speed brake was located on the fuselage bottom centerline.

Stability, control augmentation, trim and autopilot functions were provided by an Automatic Flight Control System (AFCS). Flight control power was provided by three redundant, 3,000 psi hydraulic systems

Lineup of A-7Ds of the 121st TFW, 166th TFS at Rickenbacker ANGB, Columbus, Ohio, formerly Lockbourne AFB, but renamed in honor of Captain 'Eddie' Rickenbacker in 1974. The 121st TFW received the A-7D in 1974 and traces its history to the 55th Fighter Wing established on December 7, 1947. Prior to the A-7D, this Wing has flown the P-51, F-84C, F-80, F-84E and F-100. The 166th TFS lineage goes back to December 1, 1942 with the P-39, P51-B, D and H, F-84C, F-80C, F-84E, F-84F, F-100C, D, F and finally, the A-7D. Note the Outstanding Unit Award insignia below the cockpit.

known as PC1, PC2 and PC3. A utility system [PC2] powers brakes, landing gear, nose-wheel steering, wing folding, in-flight refuelling probe, speed brake, gun firing and flaps. A ram-air-turbine (RAT) pump provides emergency back-up pressure through the PC3 system lines to operate flight controls. It also provides emergency electrical power. The RAT is wind-driven once extended into the airstream by either normal PC2 pressure or by RAT accumulator pressure.

The A-7A was powered by the Pratt and Whitney TF30-P-6 turbofan rated at 11,350 pounds of thrust at sea level. No afterburner was used as the A-7 was designed as a subsonic air-to-ground airplane. The range this engine allowed was significant although there was no excess of available power.

Company Chief Test Pilot John Konrad conducted the A-7A's initial flight at NAS Dallas, Texas on September 27, 1965. The time-frame from contract award to first flight was happily very short although some minor problems surfaced immediately. Once air-

borne on its first flight, an airframe buffet commenced which got worse with increasing airspeed. A quick return and downwind landing ensued. Apparently the flap slot areas had been obstructed creating disturbed, turbulent airflow. Retracting the flaps solved the buffet problem and a second, hour long test hop was flown without incident. Later flights proved that the A-7A had good handling characteristics but was essentially underpowered and engine performance fell off dramatically with increasing altitude.

The first production A-7s went to pilot training, Replacement Air Groups (RAGs), initially to VA-174 at NAS Cecil Field in Florida in October of 1966 and to VA-122 at NAS Lemoore, California in December. The first operational squadron to receive the A-7A was VA-147, the 'Argonauts'. Their aircraft arrived in September of 1967 and, in very short order, combat deployment to Southeast Asia was initiated on November 8, 1967 aboard the USS Ranger. On December 4, 1967 pilots of VA-147 attacked targets near

Vinh in North Vietnam on the A-7's first combat mission, only two years from date of the A-7's first flight.

Although the United States Air Force officially acquired its first YA-7Ds in April of 1968, Air Force pilots had actually flown the aircraft in combat with VA-147 on a joint service program named 'Coronet Stallion'. Further, as early as 1966, Air Force pilots had flown the A-7A model as the Air Force seriously considered the A-7 for USAF use in 1965. While these Air Force pilots found the A-7 to have excellent range and handling characteristics, experience soon showed the A-7 to be underpowered.

The Air Force was discovering that it seriously needed a true air-to-ground airplane. It had employed another Navy airplane, the venerable Douglas A-1 Skyraider, for the Southeast Asian war where it was performing the air-to-ground role better than its pure jet contemporaries. With a modified version of the A-7, the Air Force felt it would have a capable, modern attack close-air-support (CAS) airplane.

The YA-7D incorporated changes the Air Force required to improve and adapt the Naval A-7 for its needs. The powerplant was changed to the Allison TF41-A-1 turbofan which raised thrust over 30 per cent beyond that of the A-7A. This engine was a non-afterburning turbofan of Rolls Royce design manufactured by the Allison Division of General Motors. Uninstalled, sea-level static thrust was 14,250 pounds and 13,390 pounds, installed, sea-level, static, with the air-conditioning system operating.

Naval use catapult launch bars and approach progress lights were removed. The US Navy basket type refuelling probe was replaced with USAF type boom receptacle atop the fuselage. Since the airplane would no longer be carrier operated, larger wheels were installed as well as large brakes incorporating an anti-skid system.

The 20mm M61A1 six-barrel gatling type gun was installed in the lower port side of the fuselage by the air intake and replaced the

This A-7D is being readied for a bomb range mission with blue practice bombs. The right fuselage avionics bay is open, illustrating simplified ground level access. The closed panel just forward of this avionics bay covers the ram air turbine (RAT). The air intake cover is in place as the huge airscoop is susceptible to foreign object ingestion. A grounding wire is also attached.

former two, 20mm cannons. A 1,000 round-capacity drum was mounted behind the pilot's head employing a linkless feed, spent cartridges being returned to the drum rather than being ejected externally.

Tending to survivability needs, the A-7D was fitted with increased armor protection. Steel plates were installed in the nose bulkhead. Armor panels were installed in the midsection, aft fuselage and vertical tail for protection of the rudder actuator control valve, cylinder assemblies, feel isolation actuator, and horizontal stabilizer feel and control mechanism. Additional protection was provided by ceramic armor plates in the cockpit, fuselage midsection and engine bay areas. Fuel tanks were foam lined and all lines were self-sealing.

Where the A-7D would shine would be in its avionics, navigation and weapons delivery capabilities. Previously, no fighter/attack combat aircraft possessed an intrinsic computerized system for navigation and weapons delivery.

Although now *de rigueur*, the A-7D was the first American combat airplane to employ a head-up display (HUD), which displays all navigation steering, attack and landing data displays between the pilot's eyes and the windshield. The HUD supplies flight information through symbols on a combiner glass in the pilot's forward field of view. The display is in line with the aircraft flightpath and is optically focused at infinity when viewed by the pilot. HUD displays are available for *en route* navigation, attack, terrain following and landing phases.

Known as the Navigation/Weapon Delivery System (NWDS), the A-7D's new systems also included a tactical computer which computed weapons delivery solutions at thirty times per second and navigation solutions at five times per second. A Doppler

Top right: An A-7K two-seater showing the telescoping boarding ladder and additional open steps for rear seat access. The left fuselage avionics and liquid oxygen (LOX) bays are both open. A clear 'shield' was installed between the cockpits to provide blast protection to the rear seat in case of canopy loss inflight. A-7K models never served with the active duty Air Force, going directly to Air National Guard units. To become a two-place airplane, the A-7D fuselage received 34 inches in additional length.

Bottom right: Systems accessibility is clearly evident as this A-7D is virtually opened up for inspection and maintenance. The M61A1 Vulcan can be seen in the lower open panel as well as its linkless feed system rising to the 1,000 round capacity drum behind the cockpit.

Radar System provided groundspeed and drift-angle and an Air Data Computer (ADC) continuously computed altitude and airspeed data.

An Intertial Measurement Set (IMS) was the A-7D's primary gyrocompassing platform. The IMS senses aircraft heading, attitude and incremental velocity and provides these as outputs to associated avionics equipment.

A Forward Looking Radar (FLR) was installed with multi-functions of ground mapping, air-to-ground ranging for weapons delivery, terrain avoidance capability to permit maneuvering away from terrain obstacles during low-level flight and a terrain following capability to permit maneuvering at a set clearance above the terrain. In beacon mode, the radar antenna scans forty-five degrees left and right of the aircraft ground track. Transmitted radar energy interrogates airborne AN/APN-134 and ground beacon equipment.

A projected map display (PMDS) was installed, driven and controlled by the NWDS computer to display a continuous indication of aircraft position against a full-color projection of standard aeronautical charts. These aeronautical charts are cut into strips, placed end-to-end, and photographed on 35mm filmstrips for the PMDS which then moves the film to show aircraft position on the map.

Finally, an Armament Station Control Unit (ASCU) was provided to control and drop ordnance as well as fire the M61A1 cannon and provide weapon status data to the pilot and tactical computer.

The object of the entire NWDS is to integrate many of the avionic subsystems for navigation to the target, release of ordnance on target, and return. Given that the system was first used over twenty years ago, it is accurate to say that the A-7D was a true pioneer in the world of high-technology, electronic aerial warfare. The A-7D stood alone and a new era had begun.

The A-7D's first flight took place on September 26, 1968 and the first production aircraft went to the 425th Fighter Weapons

Top left: An A-7D of the 127th TFW configured with blue BDU-33, 25 pound practice bombs. The left fuselage side avionics bay is open as well as the LOX bay, its horizontally positioned door serving as a convenient 'desk' for the airplane maintenance logbook.

Bottom left: A close-up view of the A-7K's left fuselage side avionics bay showing the yellow chromate interior color. The empty air-to-air missile rail is above the avionics bay just below the wing. Below and forward of the LOX bay door is the M61A1 Vulcan gun smoke exhaust vent.

Wing at Luke AFB, Arizona on December 1, 1969. The first A-7D wing was formed in September 1970 by the 354th TFW at Myrtle Beach AFB, Florida. In October of 1972 the A-7D went into combat for the first time when the 354th TFW was deployed to Korat AFB, Thailand.

Not only did the A-7D arrive in Southeast Asia in time to participate in the 'Linebacker II' campaign, the last major offensive operation in the war, but in various roles from interdiction to gunship escort to search-and-rescue (SAR). The A-7D's work as a SAR aircraft was testimony to its ability to perform in a close-air-support and SAR arena where accuracy was paramount.

The Douglas A-1 Skyraider had been the premier, if not exclusive, SAR aircraft but many had been lost due to hostile fire and, under the 'Vietnamization' program, the remaining A-1s were destined for the Vietnamese Air Force (VNAF). In 1972 the decision was made to replace the A-1 with the A-7D in the SAR role. Training flights were performed in concert with Jolly Green rescue helicopters to refine tactics and on November 7, 1972 the A-1s flew their last SAR mission under the famous 'Sandy' callsign. Later that month the A-7Ds flew their first actual combat SAR mission.

Above: A rearward view in the right main landing gear well. Gear wells are painted white and the typical clean condition of Air National Guard aircraft is evident.

Right: An A-7K front cockpit is basically the same as that of an A-7D. Apparent is the 'vintage' instrumentation and presentation, the round-dial technology of former years *sans* modern CRT type displays. Even so, the A-7's navigation and ordnance delivery systems are excelllent.

Opposite: This A-7K is poised for a dawn training sortie as an adversary aircraft. While not a true ACM airplane, it does provide suitable harassment for the assigned flight of A-37s on a CAS training mission. The large, wide airscoop has ingested ground personnel and earned the A-7 a nickname of 'man-eater'. The small blisters beside the inlet are covers for AN/ALR-46(v) ECM warning antennas. The very narrow landing gear means crosswind landings can be difficult. The maximum direct crosswind in which landing is possible is 20 knots.

As the war drew to a close, USAF A-7s flew in the evacuation of Phnom Penh, the Mayaguez rescue, and the final evacuation of Saigon in 1975.

America's last Southeast Asian combat mission was flown by A-7Ds on August 15, 1973 as the last bombs were dropped and the last shots were fired outside Phnom Penh. With a relatively short combat tour, the A-7Ds proved rugged, versatile, reliable and the most accurate of combat attack aircraft.

Except for a few A-7s in test units, all Air Force A-7s have been turned over to Air National Guard units where further modifications were made. An automatic maneuvering flap (AMF) system was added and intended to minimize departure incidents and to provide improved turn performance. The A-7 had a tendency to depart, that is, an uncontrollable, large-amplitude yaw followed by post-stall gyrations. The next event was usually a spin entry. With this system, about five additional units of angle-of-attack (AOA) are required to create a departure as the AMF extended configuration provides increased dihedral effect and directional stability. Deployment of the leading edge flaps delays the onset of buffet below 0.7 indicated Mach number (IMN) and fifteen degrees trailing edge flaps provide from 30 to 35 per cent increase to turn performance. The AMF system ensures optimum use of flaps by automatically controlling extension and retraction of the flaps depending primarily on AOA. These deflections are tailored for best performance in the 275 to 300 knot regime at low altitude.

A Target Identification, Laser (TISL) pod was installed under the air intake and is essentially a laser-designated target detection 'Pave Penny' type system.

The two-seat A-7K was the last A-7 type produced, ending total A-7 production in September of 1984. None of these aircraft ever flew with the active duty Air Force, going directly from the factory to Air National Guard units. The 'K' model retains full combat capability as well as being trainer capable.

A taxi view through the A-7K's rear seat AN-AXQ-13 television monitor. This unit displays HUD video presentations but is designed for daylight use only and allows the back-seater to observe a straight ahead, forward windshield field-of-view, in this case the A-7D being followed. The camera is mounted on the forward cockpit's windshield frame.

The Greek Air Force ordered 60 single-seat A-7s designated the A-7H and fitted with a TF41-A-400 engine of 15,000 pounds thrust. Six two-seater A-7s were also obtained, those designated the TA-7H.

Portugal was the other foreign A-7 operator with the A-7P in the single-place configuration of which fifty were ordered, together with six two-seater TA-7Ps. These aircraft retained the two 20mm cannons and older TF30 engines from the initial A-7A/B models.

The Swiss Air Force considered A-7s in 1972 and two A-7Ds were evaluated in Switzerland but a decision was made not to purchase the aircraft.

A possible A-7 sale to Pakistan was cancelled by a former US administration under the ostensible motive that Pakistan was considering the purchase of a French nuclear reactor.

In the midst of current CAS aircraft debate, LTV has offered a variant of the A-7 with various *nom de guerre* designations such as 'Corsair III', 'Strikefighter', the 'A-7 Plus', the 'YA-7F' or the 'A-7F'. This aircraft was initially offered in mid-1985 as the solution to the Air Force's CAS/BAI requirement. The aircraft made its maiden flight on November 29, 1989 from Dallas Naval Air Station. The primary change from the A-7D is the installation of a Pratt and Whitney F100-PW-200 afterburning engine with nearly twice the thrust of the earlier engine. The fuselage was lengthened by the addition of two plugs, one in front and one in back of the wing to stretch the fuselage by 29½ inches forward and 18 inches aft. The fuel system was redesigned along with new flaps, new wing spoilers and a larger fin and rudder.

The manufacturer claims a two-to-two price advantage over the F-16, long range, heavy payload capability, and notable accuracy of navigation and ordnance delivery. Under the LTV program, some 337 A-7s would be returned to the company and modernized to the CAS/BAI version.

Aircraft 74-752, a 127th TFW, 107th TFS A-7D in the 'last chance' position before launch at Selfridge ANGB, Michigan. Ground crews are making last inspections of aircraft and ordnance. The bold black outline on the vertical fin is the VHF/Loran AN/ARC-186(v) antenna location and the black tip houses the UHF communication and IFF antenna. This airplane is on a bombing range training flight as evidenced by its BDU-33 practice bombs.

Last, it is interesting to note that while the Air Force bought the Navy's A-7, it did not take the name 'Corsair II'. It became known mainly by its A-7 designation or the 'SLUF', in polite jargon, the 'Short, Little, Ugly Fella'.

A-7D ANALYSIS

Vought's new airplane never had the fanfare bestowed to certain all-time 'favorite' glamour aircraft. But the A-7 was a harbinger of what future, attack/CAS aircraft would have to become in terms of electronic, technological capability. It did not have sleek, graceful lines, but rather a short, mean, no-nonsense look that was all business.

The A-7D offered significant technological advances that have kept its accuracy of navigation and ordnance delivery at the forefront of the field over twenty years after its birth.

It's HUD was a first and finally allowed a combat pilot to do his job without constant head-down cockpit interface. During an attack, when the pilot was task loaded, the variables of dive angle, altitude, airspeed and gunsight data were all available in the HUD. This pioneering piece of technology would eventually find its way into all modern cockpits and pilots would wonder how a mission was ever accomplished without it.

The remaining parts of the A-7D's NWDS combine to form a mighty unit that was a revolution in the 1960s, and is still exceptionally accurate to this day. This amazing system even allows the pilot to make random jinking type passes rather than long, straight-in runs as the A-7D's computer makes constant corrections to the release point for accurate results regardless of positioning.

The A-7D's range and loiter time is another favorable aspect in the equation. On an early Luke AFB, Arizona training mission, Air Force A-7D pilots flew two aircraft loaded with four MK-82, 2,000 pound bombs and 1,000 rounds of 20mm ammunition some 440 nautical miles to the Wendover Range in Utah, and returned without external fuel tanks or air-to-air refuelling, including sixty miles either side of the target flown low-level at full power! The excellent range factor and NWDS capability was proven many times in the hostile skies of Southeast Asia where there were few targets that could not be reached unrefuelled. Even three hour, over 1,000 mile, unrefuelled combat flights from Korat AFB, Thailand, occasionally took place.

Almost any ordnance can be affixed to the A-7 and the addition of multiple-ejector-racks (MERs) means a heavy and varied load can be carried. Thus, the A-7 can carry air-to-ground missiles, general purpose bombs,

Below: A 166th TFS A-7D with an AIM-9 Sidewinder missile on its left rail. This unit considers itself the first to wear the two-tone gray-on-gray camouflage finish initially displayed at the 'Gunsmoke' exercise in 1987 at Nellis AFB, Nevada.

Opposite: Flying over Michigan countryside, this profile view clearly shows the A-7D's slab sided, blunt fuselage shape. There is no doubt why the A-7 received its 'SLUF' nickname, although some official documentation refers to the airplane's 'low-profile fuselage'.

gun pods, auxiliary fuel tanks as well as air-to-air missiles. Its M-61 Vulcan cannon carries 1,000 rounds and can be fired at rates from 4,000 to 6,000 rounds per minute.

Various types of electronic countermeasure (ECM) equipment can also be carried as well as chaff and flare dispensers.

The aircraft has a high degree of maintenance accessibility with some three-dozen quick access panels, the majority of which can be reached without ground support equipment. If necessary, even a complete engine change can be performed in well under one hour.

Simply put, the NWDS *is* the A-7. The accuracy of its navigation/attack system has made the A-7 the capable performer it has been. It has been rugged and, most of all, accurate. It has been proven in the CAS environment as well.

Given all the accolades of the A-7D's navigation and bombing system, it must be realized that this capability rests inside a very old airplane. As the Air Force's interim answer to the 1960's type attack/CAS scenario, it was the right airplane. It replaced both the F-100 and the A-1 and ushered in a new era in ground attack. But, as previously discussed, the scenario and calendar has changed. The concepts that conceived the slow air-to-ground jet in the 1960s are no longer in tune with the 1990's battlefields. Unless there is total control of the sky and modern anti-aircraft defenses are absent, the A-7 has a limited chance of survival in the environment projected for future battles.

While the A-7D has received increased thrust from an upgraded engine, it still is underpowered and thrust limited. In warm, humid climates, an A-7 is hard-pressed to indicate much above 500 knots in the clean configuration and, with even a small bomb load, it is hard to reach much above 480 knots. Cold weather does allow a significant improvement over hot weather figures.

Jinking in the combat arena is usually good for one's health and, if hard maneuvering is required, whether forced by AAA or by hostile aircraft, the A-7 loses nearly 200 knots after a couple cycles and soon finds itself below 300 knots. When acceleration is demanded, the underpowered A-7 finds itself in quick trouble, a clean airplane taking about a minute and a half to accelerate from 400 knots to its maximum speed of 539 knots. These facts mean that when 'G' loading takes place, as it will in combat, the A-7 bleeds off speed dramatically. It also means that air-to-air capabilities versus modern fighters is very limited.

An Ohio ANG A-7D displays its lineage from the F-8 Crusader with its shoulder-mounted wing and general shape. Aside from some similarities, the A-7 was adopted from the F-8 and is a very different airplane.

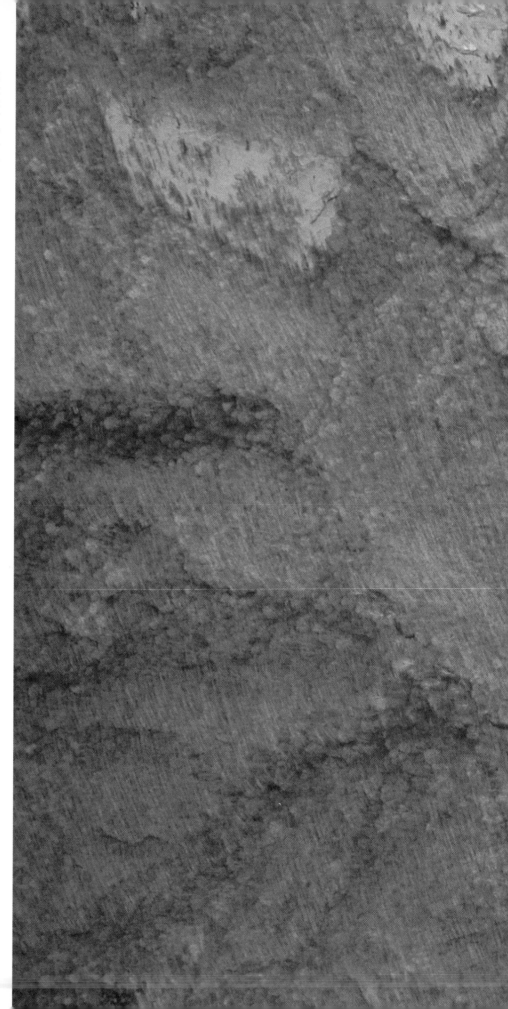

A-7 pilots still talk of good handling characteristics and air-combat-maneuvering (ACM) with their AIM-9 Sidewinders but such a scenario would have to be with early visual identification and a successful missile launch and kill before any close-in ACM took place. Some even talk of the ability to outrun hostile fighters at low altitude due to the A-7's great endurance but that would be a rather dubious plan in light of modern fighter radar technology and performance characteristics. The A-7 is simply not in the ACM class with modern fighters which now possess incredible acceleration, agility, high-sustained 'G' capability and modern air-to-air technology. Further, the A-7's rearward visibility is extremely poor should an ACM scenario develop. The modern CAS/BAI environment may well demand that entry and exit of the target area be made with increased chance of encountering hostile aircraft. The A-7 cannot survive long in that situation. In total, the A-7's threat reaction capabilities are marginal.

Obviously, the A-7 is a single-engine airplane and its survivability partially rests with that one engine functioning. While additional armor was used in the A-7D to cover vital areas, the airplane must still be considered more vulnerable in light of single versus twin-engine survivability data.

The A-7's dimensions means it is a relatively small airplane, on paper, but it has a large, slab-sided fuselage which does make it a somewhat larger target than say an F-16 which has nearly the same basic length, height and span. The silhouette coupled with slow speed means increased vulnerability to ground-to-air weapons.

As stated, the A-7Ds are old. Without any modifications the Air Force will begin retiring them in 1992. Not only has maintenance increased but its ability to do the CAS/BAI mission in future years is in serious question.

In fact, the A-7 shot itself in the foot in 1988 when a wing actually came off an airplane during a low-angle strafe pass. The A-7 fleet was grounded and cracks were found in 282 of 365 aircraft. Some A-7s never flew again while others were repaired. While the manufacturer does not admit to any design flaw or worry about the aircraft's continuing capability, a serious and obvious question

Rolling in for a low-level bomb pass, the A-7's wing weapons pylons and missile rails are revealed. Bombing accuracy is excellent with hits averaging within thirty feet of target. Visible, nose to tail, is the laser illuminated target detector (TISL) pod, the M61 Vulcan gunport, the AN/APN-190(v) doppler radar fairing with red rotating beacon attached, the UHF/ADF, AN/ARA-50 antenna fairing and the retracted, striped arresting hook.

has been raised concerning the A-7's age and its structural integrity. Continuing inspections are required, problems are still being discovered, and more A-7Ds are being permanently grounded as beyond repair.

It is fair to say that should a permissive environment prevail, the Air Force's A-7D can perform a credible job in the CAS role but its days are numbered simply due to its age and questions about structure and capability in future years. It should also be understood that, in defense of the product, the A-7D was designed as a 4,000 hour airframe and it was not until that time period was reached that the problems occurred.

Enter LTV's candidate in the new CAS/BAI aircraft search, a proposal to upgrade the A-7D to a supersonic capable, high-technology attack aircraft. This version, which various designations from Corsair III, A-7 Strikefighter, A-7 Plus and YA-7F, would be powered by an afterburning Pratt and Whitney F100-PW-220 (on current prototypes) or a General Electric GE F110 engine. Thrust would become about double that of the A-7D, which would aid in thrust response and provide a higher sustained 'G' capability.

The manufacturer initially claimed significant performance and capability increases while costs would be half that of an F-16.

Airframe alterations and additions were designed to allow the aircraft to operate from short, 3,000-foot-long, rough runways. Systems were upgraded with new fuel pumps and revised hydraulics including independence from ground support units by incorporating an internal auxiliary power unit (APU) and oxygen generating system. A Low Altitude Night Attack (LANA) system was to be installed permitting low altitude navigation and target detection day or night and under the weather.

Projected performance was a substantial increase over that of the A-7D. The new airplane was expected to sustain over 600 knots with a full ordnance load and still maneuver without speed loss. It was also said to sustain six 'G' turns up to 0.9 Mach at sea-level. Acceleration from 400 to 550 knots

was to be in the fifteen second time frame. It could also go supersonic if required.

When reality set in, the A-7D's great loiter and endurance time was greatly cut as fuel consumption was much higher than projected. Performance was about 15 per cent less than advertised at the onset and price quotes of 'half that of the F-16' turned out to be false.

Finally, even with all the work done, the basic twenty-year-old aircraft structure is still in doubt so that, even if it were at a much lower cost than its competition, the question would have to be, just what sort of airplane is being purchased? The initial upgrade program did not include replacement of the lower wing skins, where the cracks were found. New skins could be added but costs would rise again. Since the airframe would not be entirely new, there would still be doubt as to future structural problems which again questions both the feasibility and cost effectiveness of the entire modification. This airplane, when said and done, would still have a shorter lifespan and less capability overall than the F-16.

This super A-7 is currently being called the 'wild card' in the CAS/BAI aircraft competition. It was also considered to be a possible interim aircraft until a new CAS/BAI aircraft could be designed and manufactured. Since there will be no funding for that airplane, it would appear that this upgraded A-7 will fall short of becoming the next major aircraft to fill the CAS/BAI role.

The Air Force declined to send any A-7Ds to the Gulf War. While they may have had some success in the night CAS role with their low-altitude night attack (LANA) systems, the airplane was considered to be a logistical problem as there were no spare parts readily available. The A-7D is unique to the Air National Guard and the USAF is no longer able to maintain it. Further, the wing crack situation probably carried influence in the decision.

The A-7D will be retired by the Air Force in the next few years.

The overhead, top view of the A-7D shows its thirty-five degree wing sweepback, leading edge flaps, and stubby fuselage. The wrap-around gray-on-gray camouflage is shown to advantage. USAF/ANG A-7s have the same wing folding mechanism as Navy A-7s and the outer section wing fold joint outline is clearly indicated.

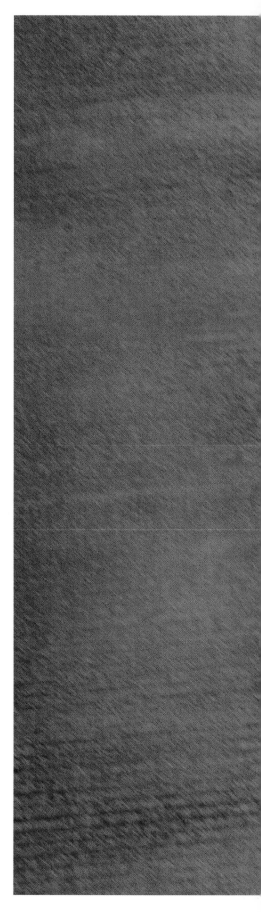

A Rickenbacker ANGB A-7D on a low-level attack profile. The A-7's excellent endurance has made it an effective CAS and attack aircraft where sustained low-level operations are required. The airplane's pug nose radome houses the AN/APQ-126(v) forward-looking radar set which has outstanding capabilities in ground mapping, terrain following and avoidance modes.

Opposite: The author's A-7K (#80-293) back-seat self-portrait with an ominous front-end view of an A-7D closing from behind. The immense airscoop takes on the look of a sinister, shark-like, hungry mouth.

Above: Literally 'on the deck', the Arizona desert is a blur at 500 knots. The aft cockpit windscreen between cockpits is clearly visible. This shield is made of clear acrylic material and provides wind blast protection if the canopy is lost. Even at this extremely low altitude and relatively high speed, the A-7 gives a smooth, air-conditioned ride to the target.

Above: An A-7K rear instrument panel photo at 330 knots over the Arizona desert floor. While the instrumentation is relatively old in design, it is straightforward and easy to comprehend at a glance. Flight instruments are centered and left while engine gauges are on the right.

Opposite: A beautiful four-ship formation by Ohio ANG, 166th TFW pilots. Major Dan Wilson leads in #247, Major Tom Dickens is number two in #191, Major Al Frierson is number three in #314, and Captain Ed Wilhoite is number four in #294. The attractive wrap-around, polyurethane, semi-gloss colors are FS 26270 — 'Neutral Gray', and FS 26118 — 'Gunship Gray'.

Overleaf: Following a bomb and strafe mission at the Atterbury air-to-ground range (R-3401) about thirty miles south of Indianapolis, the four-ship rejoins over the range with smoke still in the air.

Opposite: Returning to Rickenbacker ANGB at Columbus, Ohio, the four-ship A-7D flight has a look reminiscent of prowling attackers of the Southeast Asia vintage. Although the A-7D arrived late in that war, with its wide range of ordnance capability and exceptional accuracy, it gained an outstanding combat record in a short period. The A-7D has the distinction of having flown the final Southeast Asian combat mission over Cambodia on the morning of August 15, 1973.

Above: Banking towards initial approach for landing, these A-7Ds display the top fuselage bulge where the Air Force installed an inflight refuelling receptacle. Beauty is certainly in the eye of the beholder as A-7 pilots tend to like the airplane's aggressive appearance. They never called it the Corsair and even this flight's callsign, 'Sluff Flight', indicates their preference.

Above: Approaching Selfridge ANGB, A-7D
#71-323 displays a flat, weathered green and
gray finish typical after constant exposure to
the elements. The two basic colors are FS
34079 — 'Dark Green', and FS 36081 — 'Euro
One Gray', with black insignia, letters and
numbers.

Opposite: Tightly tucked into formation,
number two gets a close-up view as the
formation turns onto initial approach over
Lake St. Clair for an overhead pattern to
Selfridge ANGB, Michigan.

Above: Joining in formation, General Gordon Stump extends his A-7D's large belly mounted speed brake. This device can be extended and held in any position between closed and the sixty-degree fully open position. Its large size precludes ground extension so it can only be used when the landing gear handle is in the gear up position.

Opposite: An A-7D caught in the break overhead Selfridge ANGB, Michigan. The overhead pattern is flown at 300 knots with gross weight determining final approach speed which is usually just over 130 knots.

Pilots of the 166th TFS following a four-ship tactical range flight. Flightgear includes the anti-G suit, frequently called 'Speed Jeans', and the bulky, multi-pocketed survival vest, typical USAF flight gear used in Southeast Asia. Left to right is Major Tom Dickens, a full-time ANG pilot, Major Dan Wilson, a Flying Tiger Line B-727 pilot, Ed Wilhoite, a Federal Express crewmember, and Major Al Frierson, a Flying Tiger Line DC-8 pilot.

FAIRCHILD A-10 THUNDERBOLT II

It is big, bulky, and in no way aesthetically pleasing. Although officially titled the A-10A Thunderbolt II, it is generally known as the 'Warthog', or just plain 'Hog'. It frequently happens on a radio frequency check-in, that all that can be heard are pig grunts and snorts. It suffers a multitude of slanderous jokes and ridicule, such as, 'You should replace the airspeed indicator with a calendar', or 'Beware of bird strikes from the rear'.

None the less, without a doubt, the A-10 has formidable capabilities as well as a design philosophy of endurance and survivability under fire.

The need for a specialized ground attack, close-air-support aircraft was apparent during the Southeast Asian war. The need for an aircraft designed exclusively for CAS was formulated in 1966 by the United States Air Force Chief of Staff, General John P. McConnel, who asked for an attack aircraft better than the Skyraider and cheaper than the A-7D. It had to be tough, reliable, easy to repair, capable of extended loiter and be highly maneuverable.

In April of 1970 the Deputy Secretary of Defense approved the A-X (attack experimental) for competitive prototype development. A month later the Air Force issued a formal request for proposals to twelve airframe contractors inviting A-X designs. In December of 1970 the Northrop Corporation and Fairchild Industries were selected to participate in the competitive prototype development phase. In January of 1973 the Secretary of the Air Force announced that the Fairchild A-10 prototype was selected for full-scale development. The Fairchild aircraft was judged to have superior protection from gun and missile attack and to need fewer changes to make it a full production airplane than did Northrop's A-9 entry.

Fairchild's A-10 met specifications in a number of unique ways:

To enhance survivability, two engines were employed. They were mounted high on the aft fuselage, situated in close proximity such that yaw from one engine loss would not be a major problem yet far enough from each other that a hit or failure on one would not cause failure of the adjacent engine. This position also would reduce possible FOD (foreign object damage) ingestion. It also meant that a ruptured fuel cell could not spill fuel into an engine and cause fire. (This unusual engine position also partially hides the infra-red emission of the engines.) Studies of aircraft losses in combat show that if there are two engines, the loss rate due to failure of a single powerplant falls to below 2 per cent. Thus, the Fairchild design had a good start on its goal of reliability and survivability.

To protect the pilot and, it was hoped, keep the airplane flying in the event of AAA or missile hits, the design called for titanium armorplate surrounding the pilot as well as protecting vital elements of the flight control system. The pilot's 'bathtub' arrangement is made of bolted-together titanium sheets with interior faces lined with a multi-layer of nylon 'spall shield' which affords protection from fragmentation caused by direct hits. This tub is the heaviest amount of armor on the aircraft at some 1,200 pounds or about 47 per cent of the A-10's special protection weight.

Special consideration was given to the large ammunition drum for the GAU-8/A gatling gun. Due to the drum's tremendous self-destructive potential from a direct hit, about 10 per cent of the armor protection weight is used in this area. The drum was installed as far away from the aircraft skin as possible with plates of varying thickness between it and the skin so shells would explode before reaching the drum. Armor around the drum itself then protects it from fragments.

The flight control system is also unique. Twin fins and rudders are designed such that an entire stabilizer and elevator and/or fin and rudder could be lost on one side without loss of aircraft control. Also, with two fins and rudders, there is always adequate control-power available for good spin avoidance and recovery in the low-altitude environment, even if one surface is blanketed. The primary redundant hydraulic flight control system is enhanced further by a 'manual reversion' cable system, which allows the pilot to control the airplane should all hydraulics be lost.

Further adding to the survivability concept are self-sealing fuel cells protected with both internal and external foam.

On the simplicity side, the A-10's structure is conventional with approximately 95 per cent of the airframe constructed from aluminium. Single curvature skins are used on all areas aft of the cockpit permitting ease of maintenance, especially in forward operating locations. Redundant load paths are used throughout the aircraft and provide greater airframe reliability and greater damage tolerance. Numerous parts are interchangeable left and right, including the engine, main landing gear and vertical stabilizers. These attributes figure greatly in the need for quick repair operations where battle damaged aircraft need to be repaired and returned to service as soon as possible. The main cause of battle damage was considered to be the impact of high explosive devices which account for nearly 35 per cent of all potential hits. About 75 per cent of the surface area likely to be hit is designed to be replaced, the remaining areas being either resistant to damage or easily repaired. Of the replaceable areas, nearly 65 per cent can be changed within twelve hours.

Fairchild selected the General Electric TF34-100 to power the A-10 as each engine offered 8,950 pounds of thrust at a 6.1:1 bypass ratio. These powerplants provided a larger amount of power and reserve of thrust than the competition at the time and the A-10 was a big, heavy airplane.

The two engines are mounted well aft and above the airplane's longitudinal axis which could easily cause constant trim changes with the application and reduction of thrust. Thus, the engine tailpipes were angled nine degrees upwards so that their thrust passes through the average center of gravity. The TF34 has a low specific fuel consumption (SFC) so the goal of a high loiter time was achieved with times of around two hours in the battle area, versus a matter of minutes for most other jet aircraft. The engines are very quiet and said to be inaudible at anything over one mile. They are also smokeless so that telltale smoke trails are absent, a definite asset in good visibility and flat terrain. Ruggedness, reliability and maintenance have been primary considerations in the design of the TF34. Modular construction permits quick access to various engine components, and split cowls provide access to gearbox, accessories, engine blades and vanes.

The heart of the A-10's combat capability is the GAU8/A, 'Avenger', 30mm gun system and it is accurate to say that the A-10 was built around this amazing weapon. That a special aircraft design was needed to haul this gun is easy to understand when we realize that the entire assembly is nearly twenty feet long, weighs about 1,975 pounds empty, and just under 4,000 pounds with 1,170 rounds of ammunition.

The gun itself is an hydraulically-powered, gatling type mechanism. Each of the gun's seven barrels fires only once during each revolution of the barrel cluster. The GAU-8/A operates on the same principles as the 20mm Vulcan and 7.62mm minigun. Parts wear, scheduled maintenance, and a number of gun failures are all reduced through the use of seven separate barrels, with individual bolts cammed into sequential operation by simple, continuous rotary motion.

The armament system is driven by two hydraulic systems. Only one motor is used to fire the system at half rate, of 2,100 shots-per-minute. The electro-hydraulic drive system controls the clearing function and assures consistent positioning of the first live round on the feed side of the gun. The gun fires all rounds with no live rounds remaining in the chambers.

The A-10 is a big airplane. Its relative size is illustrated as this A-10 brakes into its parking spot and the ground crew and support equipment stand well below. The pilot has excellent visibility as he sits well forward under a large bubble canopy.

The linkless ammunition-feed system is used to store and feed ammunition. Spent cartridge cases and any unfired rounds are returned to the storage drum after passing through the gun. Ammunition is stored radially within the storage drum by partitions which allow rounds to move only in a longitudinal direction. The rotation of the inner helix pushes the rounds forward during system operation.

Loading of the system is relatively simple. Ammunition is loaded through a convenient access panel directly into the feed system conveyor elements.

Ammunition for the GAU-8/A gun system incorporates two new features. Aluminum cartridge cases are used instead of the conventional brass or steel to reduce weight and cost, and plastic rotating bands are used on the projectiles, since they produce much less wear on the barrels than copper bands. The Armor Piercing Incendiary (API) round has a lightweight body which contains a subcaliber high-density penetrator of depleted uranium, one of the densest substances known. The ballistics are optimized to provide the maximum remaining energy at combat ranges sufficient to defeat tanks and armored personnel carriers. The peak recoil force of this awesome weapon is some 17,000 pounds with force dropping down to 9,000 pounds at times!

While the GAU-8/A gun is considered the A-10's primary weapon, the AGM-65 Maverick now takes on an important role. This missile is electro-optically or infra-red guided and can be used some distance from the target. Once launched within the necessary parameters, the missile is on its own requiring no further assistance or guidance from the pilot, leaving the aircraft free to turn away.

It can readily be seen that a summary of the A-10's more prominent design attributes include cockpit armor, ammo drum protection, triple wing spars with redundant structure throughout, dual hydraulic flight controls with cable backup, some IR masking, spatially separated twin engines, fire/explosion proof fuel system, the tremendous firepower of the GAU-8/A Avenger gun system, and the 'launch and leave' capability of AGM-65 Maverick missiles.

Milestone dates for the A-10 start with the prototype's first flight on May 10, 1972 and the first production aircraft's initial flight on October 21, 1975. The fourth production A-10 flew on February 14, 1976 and was delivered directly to Tactical Air Command's 355th Tactical Fighter Training Wing at Davis Monthan AFB, Tucson, Arizona. In March of 1976 the USAF announced that the 354th Tactical Fighter Wing at Myrtle Beach AFB, South Carolina, would be the first operational combat-ready A-10 Wing. In December of 1976 the 333rd Tactical Fighter Training Squadron at Davis Monthan AFB graduated its first class of A-10 instructor pilots and the 354th Tactical Fighter Wing received its first A-10 in March of 1977.

The first A-10s to Europe went to the 81st Tactical Fighter Wing (USAFE) in January of 1979 and with the immense implied armor threat from the USSR, the 81st TFW received a large allocation, six combat squadrons of A-10s.

A milestone of sorts was reached in April of 1979 when the Connecticut Air National Guard received freshly manufactured A-10s, the first time an airplane was not handed down from a regular USAF unit to a Reserve organization.

In the Pacific, the 25th Tactical Fighter Squadron based in Korea received A-10s in November of 1981.

Fairchild Industries made a proposal for a two-seat A-10 and although a contract was placed for thirty aircraft, the order was cancelled as being too expensive and unnecessary. The design concept included a training aircraft as well as a night, all-weather (N/AW) combat airplane. The A-10 was considered so easy to fly that a two-seater could not be justified as a trainer but perhaps only on combat, operational grounds.

A Fairchild brochure for the time offers the two-place A-10 in numerous variants: as a night/adverse weather A-10 for low altitude penetration and target acquisition with a number of electronic modifications; as A-10 test bed in which to test advanced avionic concepts; a Battlefield Coordinator in the FAC role or that of a sensor platform; as a Defense Suppression aircraft to destroy hostile air defense systems; in a search and destroy configuration to seek out and destroy enemy command, control and communications centers; and finally, as a pure trainer for the A-10 and its CAS/attack role.

The first of the pre-production A-10s (number 73-1664) was modified into a two-seater by Fairchild with their own funds and made its first flight on May 4, 1979. The modifications took just over one year to complete and resulted not only in the second seat but also in a host of new electronic systems. The gross weight was only slightly over 2,000 pounds heavier than the standard single-place A-10A. Fairchild apparently thought there would be a need for the two-seater with its capabilities but the Air Force did not. The A-10B never went into production and the prototype remains at Edwards Air Force Base in California. A-10A funding was terminated in 1982 at a total of 707 aircraft manufactured. The last one off the assembly line was 1983 vintage.

A-10 ANALYSIS

The A-10 stands at the forefront of the current CAS aircraft debate. Can this old, big, slow, heavily armored 'tank killer' CAS airplane survive today's modern combat environment? Have new generation anti-aircraft weapons made it obsolete? Is this the age of the 'fast mover' or can the slow jets still do the job?

In the CAS role, the A-10 has an array of design attributes that make it look impressive at the onset. While many of them appear to be solid capabilities that should survive a combat milieu, unfortunately, some of its touted fortune decays in the light of current perspectives of a modern combat theater.

The A-10's dramatic use of titanium armorplate was designed and even tested to withstand direct hits from various anti-aircraft weapons. In survivability tests performed nearly twenty years ago, the A-10 was actually riddled with over 700 rounds of 23mm armor-piercing incendiary and high explosive incendiary shells, plus over 100 rounds of other calibers, all without sustaining critical damage. However, there was a good deal of selectivity on aiming points. The matter of the SA-7 Grail anti-aircraft missile was virtually dismissed by Fairchild as of 'nuisance value only'. Company gathered figures show that in the October 1973 Arab-Israeli war, twenty-six hits on Douglas A-4 Skyhawks only brought about two losses and figure that use of this weapon against the A-10 would be even less effective. That may be a rather optimistic boast.

Further, the SA-6 Gainful and later anti-aircraft missiles are a far different story. The new generation of counter-air weapons are a tough combination of mobility and lethality which even include 'flying SAM sites'. These new airborne threats have pulse-doppler radars, infra-red (IR) search and track systems (passive), and look-down, shoot-down fire control systems, and improved weapons both radar and IR. Typical of these airborne threats are MiG-23s with radar APEX and IR APHIX missiles, MiG-29s and SU-27s with the ALAMO radar and ARCHER IR missiles.

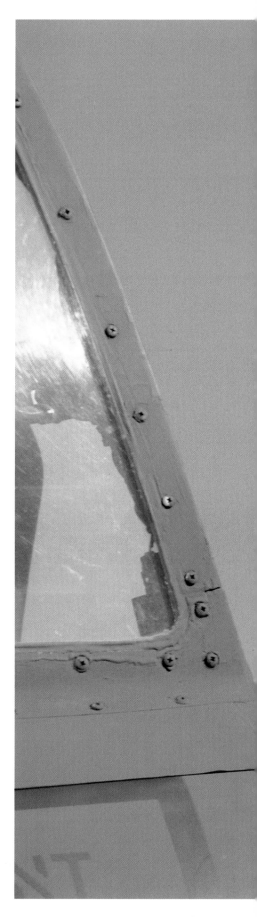

A portent of things to come, the OA-10 in the forward-air-controller (FAC) role. This 23rd TASS pilot wears the OA-10 FAC patch at Davis Monthan AFB, Tucson, Arizona. The A-10 and OA-10 are basically identical aircraft with different missions. The OA-10 will most likely receive a forward-looking infra-red system (FLIR), a wide-angle head-up display (HUD), and an automatic target handoff system (ATHS). Future OA-10s may also be fitted with a laser range finder and designation pod. The question remains whether the traditional airborne FAC mission is survivable in a modern combat environment.

Radar controlled surface-to-air missiles (SAMs) have grown from the SA-2 through the 3, 4, 6, 8, 11, 12, 15 and 17 series. IR SAMs, hand-held, include the SA-7, 14, 16 and 18 as well as the SA-9 and 13. The higher numbers basically mean improved mobility, ECCM, lethality, guidance, or combinations thereof — NOT a pretty picture! Such defenses would seriously impair the A-10's effectiveness and would have a spectacular impact on loss rates, even allowing for the use of chaff and flares. It might be possible to build a structure able to withstand the latest missiles and projectiles but an aircraft of such composition would have such degraded performance as to be virtually useless. It

Below: The GAU-8/A, 30mm, 'Avenger' from the business end. Each of the gun's barrels fires only once during each revolution of the barrel cluster with an average recoil force of 10,000 pounds. At two miles from the gun, a shell is still supersonic, still penetrates and is accurate. Inside of one mile there is virtually no bullet drop. The shell itself has a core of depleted uranium, its sole purpose being to give more mass. Weight of a single cartridge is 1.65 pounds and it has a length of just over eleven inches. The A-10 even has a front canopy water wash system to clean the canopy from residue if the gun is used frequently.

would appear that the A-10 has reached the limit of armor weight and protection versus performance.

And performance is something the A-10 lacks. The airplane does have a high degree of maneuverability, that is, roll-rate and immediate turn performance, particularly when empty, but less so when loaded. The TF-34 engines really do not provide the power required for sustained, high-energy operations, especially in hot weather. Pilots report getting into trouble in the combinations of high temperatures, constant jinking, and heavy ordnance loads. Experienced pilots have stated that the engines are 'virtually worthless on a hot day' and that they might see 280 knots maximum airspeed and perhaps be able to pull a maximum of four 'Gs'. One veteran CAS and A-10 pilot

Opposite: A close-up, underside view of the GAU-8/A, 30mm armament system. This gun is powered by two hydraulic drives operating off the two independent aircraft hydraulic systems. A linkless ammunition feed system is used to contain and feed the 30mm shells. Used cases are returned to the entrance unit on the aft end of the drum and placed back into the storage drum. Weight of the loaded system is 3,870 pounds and it has a capacity of 1,170 rounds. The entire gun system is twenty feet long.

stated that the A-10 is maneuverable, but for one time only, that in the winter he could see 380 to 390 knots in level flight but have 100 knots less in hot weather! Further, pilots have also stated that the aircraft bleeds off energy so fast that with a few good turns, low, loaded, with any real threat they would have to jettison the ordnance and evade as best they could.

The Air Force did explore the possibility of re-engining the A-10 which could provide up to a 20 per cent gain in speed and an attendant improvement in effectiveness. Unfortunately, the penalty came in the form of a 200 to 300 per cent increase in fuel consumption and a 64 per cent decrease in range. And the performance gain would still be lower than what is desired in current combat scenarios. The current A-10 has reliable and easy to maintain engines, but in all but cold weather, low altitude operations, it is simply underpowered.

One of the A-10's design features was to be the ability to operate from short trips in the forward area. It turns out that the Warthog is not a STOL aircraft. Fairchild calls the A-10's takeoff and landing parameters an 'optimization of STOL, performance, radius of action, maneuverability, loiter, large flexible mix payloads and airspeed, plus low-cost operation and maintenance'. While most imagined forward operating locations (FOLs) would have very short runways, a fully loaded A-10 can require more than 5,000 feet of runway, depending on temperature and pressure altitude. Of course, with a great reduction in the fuel load to just over 4,000 pounds and only a few bombs for ordnance, the A-10, under best circumstances of cold weather and a sea-level field, might be able to take off in just over 1,500 feet. It would then fly about fifty miles and fly a thirty minute combat mission.

In terms of self-defense, the A-10 has little to vaunt. Some pilots imagine the GAU-8/A shooting down opposition fighters but that is a remote possibility at best. Hawker Sea Furies and Douglas Skyraiders both shot down MiGs but the enemy pilots displayed great ignorance in the best use of their aircraft. It truly stretches the imagination to plan on enemy pilots slowing down to dogfight with the slow-movers. There is the potential of an adversary overshoot on a firing pass and the remote possibility of an A-10 pilot getting off a shot with the GAU-8/A. It is pure folly to count on this scenario. More likely is the use of the AIM-9L

An A-10 armament crew in action performing a required inspection of the GAU-8/A at Davis Monthan AFB. This particular examination is necessary every 25,000 rounds and necessitates removal of the gun. Barrel life is about 36,000 rounds per barrel.

Sidewinder. The outboard wing stations have been adapted to carry the missile which would certainly provide the A-10 with better self-defense capability. It would obviously be very useful if the attacking fighter pilots did not do their jobs correctly at the onset. Unfortunately, the A-10 does not even have a basic radar to identify enemy aircraft. The A-10 must be given credit for a hostile helicopter shootdown during the "Desert Storm" operation, certainly an interesting slow-mover vs slow-mover encounter.

As previously discussed, the CAS airplane will also be called upon to perform BAI functions as well as CAS roles which may take place deep in enemy territory with an inserted team. The A-10 is an airplane designed to work with the forward line of troops (FLOT) and no further inside enemy territory. Since the CAS airplane may well be asked to penetrate for some distance, the A-10 rapidly moves out of its element. Much beyond the FLOT, the A-10 is not a survivable airplane, indeed, if it is at the FLOT itself. Nor was it designed with that role in mind. But the current realities suggest that the CAS airplane may be tasked for each and all of those missions.

The A-10's weapons array is impressive. With eleven stations available, it can carry virtually any ordnance in the USAF inventory up to a maximum of 16,000 pounds external load. Exhibiting great ordnance flexibility, the A-10 can carry any combination of guided bombs, Maverick missiles, general purpose bombs, canister munitions, Rockeye, rockets, ECM pods and gun pods. And, of course, there is the internal GAU-8/A gun. If the airplane can get to the target and survive, it obviously can possess incredible firepower. There is currently some question whether the GAU-8/A has the ability to penetrate the latest in tough Soviet style armor, such as T-72 and T-80 tanks, but there is no doubt that older tanks and armor will suffer greatly under the impact of the Avenger gun, if it can get there.

While the AGM-65 Maverick missile assumes greater importance in the A-10's arsenal, a recent 1990 *U.S. News and World Report* study stated that the Maverick is one of the 'worst weapons' in the US inventory and that at a cost of $136,000 per missile and a total of $3.2 billion for 23,529 missiles, the taxpayer has been taken. The conclusion offered was that the missile has problems distinguishing tanks from fires and hot pavement. Further, boresighting and missile employment requires a high pilot workload resulting in a straight and predictable course which exposes the A-10 to not only ground-fire but also attacking aircraft. And finally, the study concludes that the Maverick will kill more pilots than tanks. The same report, none the less, concludes that the A-10 itself is one of the best weapons in the inventory due to the GAU-8/A gun and the airplane's designed survivable structure.

Pilots in the Gulf War have stated that, in fact, a true disadvantage of the Maverick is also the requirement to launch while the pilot is flying in a head-down situation. In a single-seat airplane, the pilot must not only fly but lock on to the target and fire while looking down in the cockpit. But the missile *did* work.

In the area of low, simplified maintenance and high sortie rate generation, the A-10 shines. Crew chiefs state that the A-10 is the easiest aircraft to maintain in the Air Force. Everything is simple and accessible. Specialists are not required and the feeling is that one crew chief and the airplane's pilot could keep an A-10 combat functional for days. The aircraft has its own auxiliary power unit (APU) so electric and hydraulic power plus air for engine starts and ground air conditioning is available without use of

Above: This A-10 carries a LAU-68 rocket pod which can be used by any fighter, CAS or FAC aircraft. The unit carries seven rockets, either inert HEI, API, flechett, or the 'Willie Pete' smoke rockets.

Opposite: With lower fuselage panels removed, it is obvious that the A-10's 'Avenger' gun system occupies a significant portion of the fuselage's internal area. It can be accurately said that the A-10 was designed around this gun. Pilots have found significant differences from other guns when operating this weapon. Shooting from around 6,000 feet, it takes just over two seconds until impact and on two second bursts, as they release the trigger, pilots can see rounds impacting the target through the gunsight. Depending on the type of ammunition, muzzle velocity averages 3,300 feet/second. The gun also features dual firing rates of either 2,100 or 4,200 shots per minute (SPM).

Standing fourteen feet eight inches tall, the A-10's height allows both maintenance and armament crews walk-under access for quicker, easier servicing and loading. Here, an ordnance crew loads a CBU-52 (cluster bomb unit) to the right wing inboard pylon. CBU munition is an aircraft dropped, free-fall, un-guided cluster bomb filled dispenser, designed for tactical use against personnel and light material targets. The SUU-30 is the clamshell dispenser and the CBU-52 is the entire weapon.

external units. With minimal ground support equipment, wing sections or the entire wing itself can be replaced fairly rapidly. The engines are mounted so high that they can be run without either worry about the exhaust or foreign object damage (FOD). The A-10 stands tall so that walking under the plane is no problem. Major components are located close to ground level to help facilitate inspection, servicing and maintenance. Quick-opening latches and quick-disconnect fasteners are standard features, and all access doors and panels are hinged. The GAU-8/A has easily replaceable modular components and it takes less than fifteen minutes to download and upload a full complement of ammunition. Single stores, dispensers, fuel tanks and pre-load bomb racks can be installed in about eight minutes.

From a pilot's standpoint, the A-10 is an easy airplane to fly, enough so that the two-seater trainer was never ordered for training purposes. Pilots say they feel comfortable

with the airplane quickly and that after fifteen minutes it seems as though they have had hours in it.

Flight characteristics are actually quite forgiving and even to get the A-10 to spin one must hold spin control displacement for over ten seconds. Letting go of the controls generally will allow the A-10 to fly out of a spin, assuming altitude permits.

The negative aspects emerge when high temperature and pressure altitude situations are encountered. Then, as stated previously, pilots can get into trouble. Losses have occurred following hard turns when the pilot found himself out of airspeed and could not clear terrain. One pilot was killed when he got boxed into a canyon and could not climb out.

As presented at the onset, the A-10 poses the CAS question. Most proponents of the Fairchild design refer to the European scenario, working under an overcast in bad weather with various combinations of terrain

masking — although northern Germany is fairly flat! With the latest events in Europe, that scenario may be unlikely. If it were to happen, we would seriously have to question the A-10's ability to survive in the high-technology, 1990's battleground that area would provide. With rapidly advancing progress in anti-aircraft weaponry, as discussed, the A-10 and any of its so-called 'mudfighter' potential replacements would most likely suffer totally unacceptable loss rates.

Those who wax enthusiastic about the A-10's prowess generally talk about a 1½ second GAU-8/A burst or a Maverick missile shot, then back to low-level and terrain masking before a SAM can acquire, lock-on and launch. Unfortunately, when we switch the scenario to flat, desert sands, the picture changes. The A-10 can fly low but it cannot hide. So, the A-10 pilot must evaluate the threat and adjust tactics. In the Gulf, they also flew high due to the incredible defense suppression.

This precise situation developed in the Gulf War. A-10s were sent to the Middle East due to their 'tank killing' abilities. Iraqi tanks were not the latest Soviet models so the A-10 would be expected to have great success in tank destruction *IF* they did not have to penetrate hostile airspace, and *IF* they could get to and from the target unopposed and not face the latest in air defense systems. With free reign of the sky, the A-10s did well against ground targets, the mission they were designed to perform.

Unfortunately, a great number of those who tout the A-10's capabilities still envision conflicts of the Korean or Southeast Asian caliber before the age of electronic, technologically sophisticated warfare. The concept of a relatively slow CAS aircraft, survivable by low flight, terrain masking, special armor and redundant systems finds validity today and in the future within very narrow parameters, many of which are highly unlikely.

An armorer's table at the Ft. Drum forward operating location (FOL). Six olive drab MK-82 500 pound bombs await loading onto A-10s. The yellow rings indicate live munitions. An A-10's empty weight is 25,600 pounds but its maximum gross weight is 51,000 pounds including a maximum load of 16,000 pounds. These MK-82 bombs are configured as MK-82 AIRs (Air-Inflatable-Retards). The A-10's eleven pylons allow virtually several hundred combinations of stores. This Maryland ANG A-10 is already configured with a CBU.

Of course, the Gulf War was one of those highly unlikely wars, one that should not happen, with slow-movers, air FACs, and multiple passes. But, the main reasons for success were complete air-superiority and the ability to traverse the battlefield virtually at will, awesome defense suppression, high-technology equipment, improved tactics — and a war in which the outcome was inevitable. Only the questions of how long and at what cost remained. When we consider a serious high-threat, bad weather environment, the Gulf War must be viewed as an anomaly and drawing overall, far-reaching conclusions from it will be an error.

IF we are allowed to select our conflicts and set battle conditions, then the A-10 and any of its follow-on derivatives are capable and effective when unopposed by enemy aircraft, when the ground-forces do not have the latest in surface-to-air weapons, and when the targets are composed of relatively old armor. If these conditions are not met, the A-10 is a highly vulnerable slow-mover.

Numerous A-10s are being assigned to the FAC role and some were used in Operation Desert Storm. The Air Force expects to have 220 of them operational in 1991. While we have said that the traditional FAC scenario cannot be expected to work in the modern battlefield, the OA-10 may serve well in a 'stand-off' position, not only able to relay communications and electronic data but also to transmit information via an automatic target handoff system (ATHS). Currently, three forward-looking infra-red systems are being evaluated for the OA-10.

In a fairly permissive environment, the A-10 also may be called into play in the rescue role. It found some use in the Gulf War in that role even going so far as to use the Skyraider's "Sandy" callsign.

The A-10 has been unique in that no other country has ordered the airplane. In mid-1990, Greece and Turkey expressed interest in obtaining some A-10s which would otherwise have been retired under a Conventional Forces Europe Treaty. While the A-10 may be newer and somewhat more capable than aircraft some nations now operate, the allied governments still show appropriate scepticism concerning the A-10 and its niche in modern warfare. At this time, the Air Force is looking at retaining two wings of A-10s although no long-term decision has been made to retain any A-10s.

Opposite: The A-10's instrument panel and head-up display (HUD) on top. Although not a state-of-the-art 'glass' cockpit, this instrument panel is straightforward and easy to comprehend. The three handles below the HUD are the fire handles for both engines plus the auxiliary power unit (APU). Flight instruments are centrally located and flanked by an armament control panel on the left and engine instruments on the right.

Below: Fairchild and the Air Force may have called the A-10 the 'Thunderbolt II' but to its pilots it will always be a 'Hog' in one form or another. This Baltimore, Maryland 175th TFG pilot wears a shoulder patch depicting the grotesque, ungainly 'Warthog' and its 30mm gun.

Overleaf: As the name suggests, a forward operating location (FOL) is a venue close to the battle with austere surroundings and accommodations but capable of supporting CAS/attack aircraft with ordnance, limited maintenance and sufficient runway. The concept is particularly linked to the European battle scenario with FOLs in Germany, for example. The A-10 sits in a training FOL at Wheeler-Sack Army Airfield at Ft. Drum, New York. The location even has the look of a typical European setting.

Above: About to begin taxi for takeoff, this pilot has his navigation and tactical charts stowed by the forward canopy. The integral boarding ladder is still extended with its door open. The ladder telescopes under gravity when the door opens.

Opposite: The Warthog's peculiar aft view illustrating the unusual engine configuration. Essentially, the two General Electric TF34-100 turbofans are not part of the fuselage. Loss of an engine, or the pod itself, should not cause further structural damage or affect the other engine. The engine itself weighs 1,427 pounds, is 100 inches long (8.33 feet) and has a diameter of 49 inches. The rectangular object on the fuselage between the pods is the pre-cooler intake duct.

The Hog's rather foreboding front end view as it taxis into a FOL revetment at Ft. Drum. The awesome GAU-8/A gun is clearly offset nose left which keeps the firing barrel on the centerline. Thus, the nose gear is offset to the right. As formidable as the A-10 appears, there is considerable argument that it cannot survive a 1990s European combat environment, although that scenario appears unlikely at present. And we cannot conclude that future battlefields will offer the complete air-superiority and defense suppression environment of the Gulf War. The big CAS question is what should the A-10's replacement be?

Above: The Willow Grove, Pennsylvania A-10 ANG unit patch. Formerly the 111th TASG, 103rd TASS, flying the OA-37, it then received the OA-10 and became the first ANG OA-10 FAC designated organization. The pilots responded by re-naming themselves the 'Black Hogs'.

Opposite: Maryland ANG A-10 number 719 parking in the FOL area at Ft. Drum, New York. Already open on the upper left main gear position is the cover for the aircraft single-point refuelling controls. The dark circular dot on the aircraft's nose is an AN/ALR-69 radar warning system antenna. Speed brakes are still extended on the right wing. The large pylon below the cockpit extending down below the fuselage is designed to carry the Pave Penny laser spot tracker. If another source illuminates the target with a laser designator, the Pave Penny system picks up the reflected energy and displays the designated target on the pilot's head-up display (HUD).

An A-10 at liftoff from the FOL at Ft. Drum. This runway is 5,000 feet long and adequate for an A-10 with a maximum ordnance load. A measure of design emphasis was placed on shortfield performance (even being called short-takeoff-and-landing (STOL) by some) with capability to operate from unpaved front-line FOL airstrips. The production outcome is not a STOL airplane and even with small loads and much reduced fuel, the A-10 requires nearly 2,000 feet of runway.

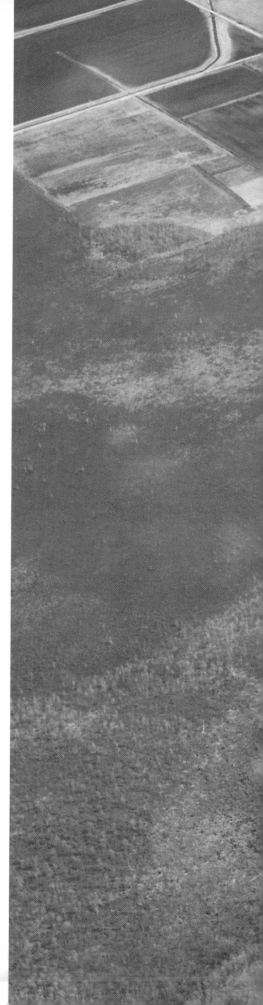

Above: Serial number 78-670, a 1978 vintage A-10 from the Syracuse, New York ANG unit, the 'Boys From Syracuse', shortly before the unit transitioned to the F-16. Flown by Colonel T. J. Costello, this particular airplane wears special 'Bavaria' decorations indicating it has actually been in Bavaria on Tactical Air Command's (TAC) 'Checkered Flag' exercise simulating a NATO deployment. To have crews realistically trained in the European theatre, the unit went on temporary duty (TDY) to Fighter-Bomber Wing (FBW) 32 at Lechfeld located about thirty miles west of Munich. The German Tornado unit has become a 'sister' organization to the Syracuse ANG and only the A-10s that actually went to the European deployment were allowed to have the Lion and 'Bavaria' painted on the aircraft. To this particular aircraft was also added a blue and white 'Bavarian check' pattern signifying that it was the commander's jet.

Opposite: Since its inception, a great deal of variation has gone into the A-10's camouflage schemes. Because the airplane would operate from high to low altitudes in a variety of locations, several combinations have been tried, from gray to spotted to what has become its present garb. This operational color was first known as 'Lizard' but officially became 'European One', a combination of FS 34092 — 'Euro One Dark Green', FS 36081 — 'Euro One Gray', and FS 34102 — 'Medium Green'. The paint is a radar-absorbing polyurethane from stealth technology manufacture. Obviously the bulky, huge A-10 needs all the stealth technology it can get.

The A-10's semi-retractable landing gear is clearly evident in this underside photo. Part of the main gear is exposed, a design objective that less damage would be done in the event the aircraft sustained a gear-up landing. Also shown are the eleven hardpoints, four under each wing and three under the fuselage. Clearly visible is the drooped wingtip designed to improve aileron efficiency at low speeds. Also prominent are the full-length rudders and huge engine nacelles. By the aft center navigation light is another AN/ALR-69 radar warning antenna. The Warthog is a most interesting, if unsightly design. It found its cause célèbre in Operation Desert Storm where air-superiority and virtual defense suppression allowed it to have a field-day against the Iraqis. It would have been a magnificent CAS/SAR airplane in the permissive days of the Southeast Asian conflict.

GENERAL DYNAMICS
F-16 FIGHTING FALCON

Since rollout of the Full Scale Development (FSD) F-16 in October of 1976, the Falcon has forged an illustrious, multi-faceted reputation in military aviation history. From its birth as the winner of the Lightweight Fighter (LWF) competition it has become a veritable air force within itself with capable if not superior performance in aggressor/adversary duties, interception, air-to-air, defense suppression, reconnaissance, attack and close-air-support. In less than five years from initial production the F-16 was assimilated into the air forces of nine nations. It has become a legend in its own time as the 'fighter pilot's fighter' and it may well be known in the future as a talented, competent, if not superior close-air-support aircraft that can play hardball in our technologically advanced combat environment.

Several events motivated tactical planners into development of the lightweight fighter concept. One was the staggering decline in the kill ratio experienced by US pilots in the Southeast Asian war versus the Korean war. The enemy had small, agile fighters in great numbers with good dogfighting capabilities. US aircraft were large, heavy, and complex with reliance on air-to-air missiles rather than guns and maneuverability. US pilots soon discovered that their missiles had to be launched within narrow parameters to work as advertised and, even then, the failure rate was excessive. And once missiles were spent, most airplanes did not possess a backup weapon.

In 1970, US aerospace industry responded to Air Force requests to study energy maneuverability, and other aerodynamic technologies that could be used in future fighters. Feasibility of these concepts was tested by prototype aircraft. In April of 1972, General Dynamics and Northrop began building two YF-16s and YF-17s respectively. The overall goal was to apply advanced technology in straightforward ways to achieve performance objectives in a lightweight fighter aircraft.

The Mideast war of 1973 also provided the realization that sheer numbers of fighter aircraft could be as critical as performance. But there was no way to have large numbers of complex, expensive airplanes. Again, thought was directed at a lightweight, agile, lower-cost fighter.

A fly-off against Northrop's YF-17 took place during 1974 and results were tabulated in December of that year. On January 13, 1975 the Air Force announced that the General Dynamics product had been selected based on both performance and cost. Pilots involved in the contest spoke in glowing terms of the F-16's incredible maneuverability, greater excess thrust, and even superior range. During these trials, the YF-16 was also flown against a variety of adversary aircraft for evaluation of aerial combat performance in simulated dogfights and interceptions. At the onset, a Cessna A-37 was used to evaluate the F-16's performance versus a low wing-loaded aircraft in the low-altitude environment. Then it flew against the F-4E, a MiG-17, a MiG-21 and most likely other Soviet-manufactured fighters, to check performance in higher altitude combat. The final evaluation was against the Convair F-106 in a high-altitude interceptor role. As to the outcome, the director of the F-16 joint test force commented, 'The problem is, we haven't any aircraft that is a real challenge to the F-16 other than another F-16.'

As recent combat experience had shown, the necessary ingredients for successful fighter combat involved turning performance, high acceleration, more reliable fire-control systems and armament, plus better range. The F-16 certainly had them all and the cost was right.

The Falcon's futuristic shape was the result of a merger of the latest in technological advancements. Estimates conclude that use of these advancements in the F-16 saved about 1,300 pounds in empty weight and 2,200 pounds in gross weight when compared to other designs. In early 1977 figures, General Dynamics put cost per airframe structural pound at only $60.00.

Numerous innovative design features were incorporated into the F-16 and gave it a shape like futuristic space vehicles seen in science-fiction motion pictures.

Rather than traditional, sharper, angled wing-to-fuselage joints, a unique wing-body blending was chosen to provide greater body lift and fuel volume. A shorter fuselage and a weight saving of nearly 400 pounds was thus achieved.

Forebody strakes provided controlled vortex lift. Trim drag was reduced and generated vortices gave additional lift as well as improved airflow over the tail. A wing with more area would be required to gain similar advantages and would add nearly 500 pounds.

Variable wing camber allowed a smaller, thinner wing and was achieved by use of automatic maneuvering flaps which change wing camber to maintain optimum lift at high angles of attack. The benefits to maneuverability are higher maximum lift capability, lower drag at a given lift, improved directional stability and significantly improved buffet characteristics. In addition, flaperons are mounted on the trailing edge and combine the functions of flaps and ailerons.

Number 79-0401, a 174th TFW, 138th TFW F-16A at Hancock Field, Syracuse, New York. This Block 10 aircraft was production number 417 and its delivery date was in May of 1981. The first two digits of an Air Force aircraft's serial number actually denotes the airplane's funding year. The orange (FS 32356) ejection seat warning placard points down to the M61A1 20mm cannon gun port and fairing with its purge gills and holes. The wingtip Sidewinder launching rail is empty, as is the triple ejector rack (TER) on the underwing pylon.

Relaxed static stability (RSS) was another unique feature integrated into the F-16 and was achieved by use of the fly-by-wire (FBW) flight control system. In its more basic explanation, RSS means the aircraft's center of gravity has been moved aft behind the center of lift causing the aircraft to be unstable. Conventional airplanes have positive stability and any deviation from level flight is automatically offset by horizontal tail loading. The penalty is drag.

The General Dynamics thought was that they did not want the horizontal stabilizer to be fighting the wing during turns. Once the turn and loading is established with the F-16, the tail returns to a neutral position and the wing, tail and fuselage are all acting as lifting surfaces, which means the airplane turns very well and even accelerates well during the turn. RSS reduces trim drag and even allows the aft fuselage and tail to be lighter. In the F-16, about a 400 pound weight saving was gained in this area. General Dynamics says RSS in the F-16 translates into a 15 per cent greater supersonic turn rate and 8 per cent better subsonic turn rate with higher response rates than conventional aircraft.

While RSS has advantages, it cannot be achieved with a manual flight control system as a pilot would be unable to control the airplane. The FBW system reacts instantly due to its electronic architecture, has ample power and authority and with its four-channel, quadruple redundancy, the F-16's FBW system means better handling, exceptional agility and control response as well as a simplified aircraft structure which no longer has to accommodate the linkages and cables of a normal control system.

A side-stick controller was applied to the F-16 and is actually a minimum-displacement force sensing stick. The pilot's arm is in a support rest and his hand pressure electrically signals actuators and servos which move control surfaces.

A high-acceleration, high-visibility cockpit environment was mated to the design. Since the F-16 would be able to sustain very high 'G' performance, improved pilot stress tolerance was gained by use of a seat tilted backwards thirty degrees coupled with a raised lower body and foot position. While a further reclined seat near the sixty-five degree position may be optimum, the thirty degree position provided a good compromise which allowed continued use of normal cockpit instrumentation presentation as well as ejection seat installation and operating parameters.

The F-16's head-up display (HUD) gives steering to selected turn points for inertial navigation as well as heading, airspeed, altitude and flight attitude information. It also offers time and distance to targets in nautical miles plus minutes and seconds. Additional displays are g-loading, Mach number, the weapons delivery mode selected on the digital stores management system and a target designator (TD) box.

The large, clear bubble canopy permits virtually unobstructed forward and upward vision and at least fifteen degrees over the nose, forty degrees down at the sides, and superb rearward vision. The canopy itself is one-piece and constructed with one-half inch polycarbonate.

The distinctive lower-air-inlet scoop was the result of many tests to find the best solution to the problems of airflow in the high transonic and supersonic regions. Versus other designs, the F-16's inlet configuration, *sans* any variable geometry, provided less weight and drag, less expense, simplicity, and a higher overall maneuver potential. Foreign object damage (FOD) potential was greatly reduced by installation of the nose gear aft of the inlet which eliminates matter thrown up by the nosewheel.

Of engines considered at the time, the F-16 design team felt the Pratt and Whitney F-100 was the best choice. For lower weight it offered superior performance consistent with aircraft design objectives. An obvious advantage was that the same engine was already used in the F-15 and funds would be saved by not developing, testing and maintaining a new type powerplant. The F-100 was proven and in full production. This afterburning turbofan is in the 25,000 pound thrust class, providing 25 per cent more power per pound of engine weight than the best previous fighter engine. The engine weighs just under 3,000 pounds and has a high installed aircraft thrust-to-weight ratio of 1.1:1 which means the F-16 has exceptional acceleration and maneuverability with a top speed of over Mach 2, straight up, vertical acceleration, and the ability to attain 9 'Gs'. It is also virtually smokeless.

As can be seen, the technologies applied to the F-16 were selected and integrated in such a way as to simplify the airplane and reduce weight by several thousand pounds as well as reduce cost.

The light weight of the F-16 was achieved without use of exotic materials or degradation in strength. It was even recognized that strategic materials such as titanium could be

A closeup of the large fixed-ramp air intake inlet below the fuselage. The internal strut serves to aid structural rigidity and is even heated for anti-ice protection. Note the nose gear mounted aft of the inlet which helps prevent FOD ingestion. Engine running suction forces are high and there is a twenty-five foot danger area in front of the nose under operating conditions. Ground personnel *have* been picked up and ingested! The bulged fairing forward of the 'rescue' arrow covers a threat warning antenna (RHAW). The angle-of-attack (AOA) probe protrudes from the aft radome area and below it is a pitot sensor for the air data computer.

in short supply or perhaps not available and extensive use was avoided. The structure is over 78 per cent aluminum with 0.5 per cent titanium, 11 per cent steel, a little over 3 per cent advanced composites and about 7 per cent other materials. Structural capability is provided to give a design load limit of 9 'Gs' with full internal fuel, a further result of General Dynamics making its Model 401 25 per cent overstrong.

F-16 ease of maintenance was a design consideration and about 60 per cent of the skin has removable panels to allow access to the majority of internal components. Further, some 228 quick-entry doors are provided.

There are 380 interchangeable parts on the F-16. Identical horizontal tail surfaces, ventral fins and wing flap/ailerons are used for both sides of the airplane and are completely interchangeable. Even most of the main landing gear can be used on either side.

Chosen as the F-16's basic, internal weapon was the venerable General Electric M61A-1 20mm multi-barrelled gun mounted in the left wing-to-fuselage fairing. This gun fires 6,000 rounds per minute and has a 515 round supply. Considered standard armament are AIM-9L/M Sidewinder heat-seeking missiles mounted on wingtip rails. A rather wide array of external munitions can be carried on the aircraft's ordnance stations for a maximum of 12,000 pounds with a full fuel load. The variety of weapons include conventional bombs, CBU, laser and TV-guided weapons, countermeasure pods and the General Electric GPU-5/A 30mm gun pod.

Initially flown on August 8, 1977 the two-seat F-16B was able to retain the same dimensions as the F-16A but sacrificed internal fuel by 1,300 pounds or almost 19 per cent. The F-16B essentially retains the same performance characteristics and combat capability of the single-seater aside from reduced internal fuel and loss of range.

Externally, the F-16C looks little different from the 'A' model but interior changes are significant. While the F-16A has the APG-66 multimode fire control radar, the improved APG-68 radar was installed in the 'C'. This unit has sophisticated air-to-air modes and air-to-ground modes such as track-while-scan, expanded resolution, better doppler beam sharpening, and ground moving target mode.

Seven 174th TFW F-16s on the Hancock Field ANG ramp. The Syracuse unit received Block 10 aircraft. 'The Boys From Syracuse' markings have endured since the days of the F-86s. The F-16's vertical tail has an aluminum spar and rib structure with graphite-epoxy skins. The upper protrusion on the vertical tail's base fairing is a threat warning (TWS) antenna cover and the white tail position light is just below.

Further improvements came in electrical power, cooling, structure, wiring, and a wide-angle HUD with 50 per cent larger total field of view with ability to display FLIR imagery for night operations was a large improvement. Other enhancements include greatly improved pilot/vehicle interface avionics such as two multi-function displays, up front controls for accessing communications and navigation information, and a data transfer system used to load mission planning information into the aircraft computers with the push of a button. The F-16C also allows a choice of advanced engines for even higher performance.

On January 6, 1979, the first operational F-16A went to the 388th TFW at Hill AFB, Utah. The first overseas bound F-16s went to the 8th TFW at Kunsan AFB, South Korea on June 26, 1981. Numerous countries operate and even manufacture the F-16 and Israel gave it its first taste of combat when eight F-16s attacked Iraq's nuclear power plant on June 7, 1981.

The US Air Force Aerial Demonstration Team, known as the Thunderbirds, transitioned to the F-16 in November of 1982 and flew their first F-16 show in April of 1983.

The US Navy selected the F-16, to be known as the F-16N, as its adversary flight training aircraft in January 1985 and they were delivered to the Naval Fighter Weapons School ('Top Gun') and VF-126 at NAS Miramar, California in June of 1987.

The latest F-16 role is in CAS and the Air Force selected the New York Air National Guard's 174th TFW at Hancock Field, Syracuse, New York, as a prototype unit to determine how best to further refine the F-16 in that mission. The Syracuse ANG has a history of CAS roles from its F-86 days through the recent A-10 which may have had some import on the unit's selection as the first F-16 CAS outfit.

Although controversy lingers, sceptics abound, and bureaucrats and politicians proliferate, demonstrations have confirmed that a fast, agile jet *can* do the CAS mission when equipped with modern electronic technology. Eventual, planned updates to the F-16 as a CAS airplane include an automatic target handoff system (ATHS), a Pave Penny laser-spot-tracker targeting system plus a better automated maneuvering and attack system (AMAS). The Westinghouse APG-68 radar and a digital, three-dimensional terrain map system may be installed in later models.

Falcon Eye, a head steerable IR sensor to provide a high-threat, low altitude, night maneuvering capability, is also being considered.

Below: The Pratt and Whitney F-100 jet pipe exhaust nozzle detail. The metallic blue rings at the base are the natural colors of that alloy through heat distribution. The afterburner's petals are known as 'turkey feathers'. The nozzle is in the closed, small opening, position at idle power and opens when afterburner is selected. An exception to this is that the nozzle opens near idle power with the gear down to reduce residual thrust for landing and taxiing. At idle, fifteen feet behind the exhaust, wind blast velocity is 120 knots and greater than 200 degrees F.

Opposite: The F-16's horizontal stabilizers have an aluminum substructure with graphite-epoxy skins and are interchangeable side to side. They are single piece, all moving pieces. Speedbrakes are inboard of the stabilizers and can open up to sixty degrees in two to three seconds. On fuselage bottom centerline is a 300 gallon fuel tank. The narrow wheelbase of seven feet nine inches means crosswind landing can be trying. The textbook maximum crosswind for landing is 25 knots.

ANALYSIS

While there is little question of the F-16's prowess as a superb air-to-air dogfighter, there are a number of doubters who say its virtues do not include CAS.

At the onset we have said that funding will simply not be available to conceive and manufacture a new, state-of-the-art CAS airplane. Even if we allow the fiction that the money would somehow appear, two major considerations emerge:

First, at this point in time anyway, the debate has not been settled on whether such an airplane should be a slow-mover A-10 sort of weapon, an agile F-16 type, or a force of both types used together.

Second, as previously stated, in the US, such a new design would fly in ten to twelve years — at which time it would certainly be bogged down in political 'add-ons' and not be the airplane first conceived. Additionally, given such incredible time from inception to reality, the pace of anti-aircraft technology would probably have surpassed the capabilities of the design. At that point we might even be dealing with remotely-piloted vehicles and the manned CAS airplane could be a museum piece.

Fiction aside, certain realities must be faced. The battlefields are no longer permissive. Although the Vietnam type combat environment is twenty years old, there are those, both Army and Air Force, who still think the CAS pilot should be overhead in his heavily-armed, slow-moving attack-bomber, providing constant support. As has been pointed out, this scenario will most likely never happen again. With mercurial advances in surface-to-air weaponry, the pilot's slogan finds even more meaning — 'SPEED IS LIFE'.

Now and in the future, if the CAS mission can be accomplished successfully (and in some cases it may not be viable at all), required survivability will hinge on agility, high-speed and acceleration capacity, electronic packaging, countermeasures, ordnance delivery accuracy, the ability to take a hit without catastrophic consequences, and even the capability to engage and defeat enemy aircraft on both ingress and egress.

The F-16 has a wide speed range and, top-end, can accurately be called a 'fast jet'. With ordnance, it can fly relatively slow at about 250 knots if required, yet has very high acceleration and dash ability to near 600 knots in less than twenty seconds. On CAS exercises, a defense tracker operating advanced AAA equipment confirmed that, although it does not take long, one must still acquire the target aircraft, get set up and lock on, not an instantaneous process. He cited the F-16 as small, agile, very fast, and that it was not possible to keep it in his sights very long, and sometimes not at all. Further, due to its small size, the F-16 is hard to detect from the ground visually or with radar and therefore hard to hit. It also vividly aids the element of surprise.

Sceptics, including a number of fast-jet pilots experienced in past conflicts as well as training exercises, say it is very difficult, if not impossible, to locate a target, set up, then strike in the time allotted by high-speed flight. Those are honest and true sentiments. Unfortunately, the high-technology arena the CAS pilot now faces precludes most forms of leisurely target perusal and cavorting with a FAC overhead, a fact applicable to both slow and fast movers.

The CAS pilot cannot afford the luxury of flying slow in the effort to locate his target. Enter the ATHS, basically a modem connecting an aircraft to its data system. It can link up with multiple networks on various frequencies and pass information traditionally provided by a FAC including target type, location, where the friendlies are and any special attack information. This data can be sent by ground-based personnel, helicopters, or a communications relay of FAC type aircraft. The information is relayed through a digital data link which completely avoids voice communication and is entered automatically into the F-16's fire control computer, then displayed on the HUD. The older, voice communication method could take a minute or more but ATHS delivers in seconds and gives the F-16 pilot a nine line HUD briefing and, with inertial navigation system (INS) guidance, allows an effective, accurate first pass identification and strike. The ATHS can even update target coordinates as close as thirty seconds before time over target in case of a change in target or a moving one. As to the old visual target acquisition plight, now the pilot does not even have to see the target and, with smoke or other obscuration, he may not. ATHS is a major force in workload and time reduction.

An obvious criticism and potential problem is that the exchange of accurate target information between ground and air could break down. A voice backup with its delays and faults could then be used.

Far better would be the Pave Penny system which can work in conjunction with ATHS or as a separate device. Basically, a laser spot is put on the target by ground forces or from the air. The aircraft receiver translates the spot to the pilot's HUD in the form of a target designator (TD) box. The target is well

An F-16B loaded with an AIM-9L Sidewinder plus a triple ejector rack, TER-9A carrying a load of BDU-33D/B twenty-five pound practice bombs. These blue colored bombs carry a smoke charge so impact is noted by a puff of white smoke for scoring purposes. The AIM-9L is a later model Sidewinder with long span, double-delta controls.

On fuselage centerline is the streamlined GPU-5A gun pod containing the GAU-13/A 30mm gun. This gun has a linkless, closed-loop concentric helix feed system with a self-contained drive system. The four-barrelled gatling type gun is 100 inches long and weighs 341 pounds. With a loaded weapon, the pod weighs 1,905 pounds. Although it carries only 353 rounds, from thirty to fifty rounds are usually expended in one burst, which means eight or nine solid bursts are available, comparable to most any gun, past or present.

defined to the foot, is inside the TD box, and can be revised constantly or re-directed to another, specific target and ensures accurate target designation in a fluid CAS scenario.

Pilots returning from Operation Desert Storm express great enthusiasm for the F-16's CAS/Interdiction abilities under fire and feel that an A-16 tied in with a Joint-STARS aircraft using digital modem transfer would have been spectacular. In this theater, aircraft directed by Joint-STARS had a 90% success rate in finding targets on the first pass.

While the F-16 can carry an extensive and varied ordnance load from unguided iron bombs through laser and TV-guided weapons, a typical 'soft' CAS load would most likely be a combination of CBU, missiles, the GAU-13/A 30mm gun plus the 20mm internal gun and AIM-9L Sidewinders for self-protection.

That the F-16 can deliver ordnance accurately can be seen by the 'Gunsmoke' competitions of recent years where the F-16 leads every other aircraft type. Gunsmoke is a Tactical Air Command, biennial air-to-ground gunnery meet with profiles from the conventional range box-pattern through tactical bomb delivery to navigation and attack. The F-16 is a consistent winner. In the world of actual combat, on June 7, 1981, the Israelis flew F-16s to Iraq and destroyed the nuclear reactor at Osirah near Baghdad. Then, in 1982, over Lebanon, Israeli F-16s accounted for about fifty Syrian warplanes of which most were MiG-21s and MiG-23s.

For comparison purposes, the F-16 has twice the range of the venerable F-4 Phantom with the same payload including accuracy with unguided bombs of almost four times greater than the F-4 and as good if not better than the A-7. Also, if required, the F-16 flies fast enough to generate enough energy to toss free-fall munitions some distance. With its standard fire control modes including a constantly computed release point (CCRP), the claim is that at 500 knots, the F-16 can

toss a 500 pound MK-82 bomb four or five miles fairly accurately. The obvious questions any groundforce would ask is what does 'fairly accurately' really mean and in a CAS/TIC scenario, the definition could have serious import and such measures would probably not fall within the CAS profile. An A-10 or similar 'mudfighter' design cannot go fast enough to toss free-fall ordnance a significant distance.

The GAU-13/A 30mm gun carried in the F-16's GPU-5A gun pod is a four-barrel gatling type weapon with a capacity of 353 rounds and a firing rate of 2,400 shots per minute (SPM). The gun shoots an average of 30 to 50 rounds in one short burst. While the usefulness of carrying a 353 round capacity gun in a pod has been called into question, it turns out to have accuracy comparable to the A-10's much touted gun. In addition, it has less vibration than is felt in the A-10, is very reliable, like any gun, it cannot be counter-measured, and has the advantage of being mounted below the airplane where smoke generated by firing the gun does not impede the F-16 pilot's visibility. Further, the F-16 is a formidable air-to-air fighter and the GAU-13/A is effective in that region as well as air-to-ground, a potential added bonus.

Obviously, some performance degradation will occur as the F-16 carries a CAS load to its target and its ability to be a real dogfighter is downgraded as well. These are legitimate concerns but it should be remembered that, even with ordnance, the F-16 is faster than anything else in the CAS role. In a worst-case scenario, should the CAS airplane be attacked before reaching its target, it may have to jettison ordnance in order to evade or fight. But in such circumstances, *any* CAS type would have the same survival option. Mission viability is certainly called into question in such situations where continued flight to the target means being shot down. A downed aircraft does not help the troops or the pilot.

Close-up of the TER-9A triple ejector rack. This versatile rack can carry up to three conventional munitions in the 500 pound class such as MK-82 high and low drag bombs, CBU cluster munitions, MK-20 Rockeye anti-armor bomb canisters, or LAU-68 rocket pods.

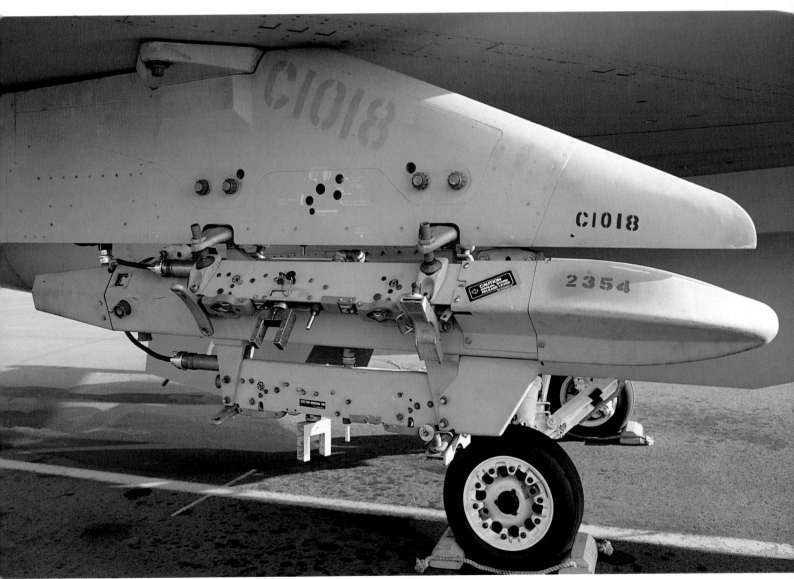

Opposite: The F-16A cockpit. Below the HUD, directly centered, is the HUD control panel. Flight instruments are below and to the right side. The screen below is the radar electro-optical display. The large monitor on the left is the stores control panel for weapons. The unique sidestick controller is on the right and behind it is the arm rest to support the pilot's arm during high load maneuvering. Pilot workload was greatly reduced by this layout and presentation which has been called the best fighter cockpit ever designed. The F-16 cockpit has no circuit breakers, quite a break from traditional cockpit layout.

Below: The F-16B rear instrument panel. Note its simplicity when compared to older cockpit layouts. The intent is to allow the pilot to manage systems effectively and rapidly and keep a heads-out orientation to do the mission at hand. The central, green tinted video screen is a radar display that provides a view through the HUD via a video camera. In this photo, the camera picks up the landscape ahead of the aircraft as seen through the forward cockpit's HUD. To the left of the screen is the stores control panel or stores management system (SMS). As set, it shows an AIM-9L/M Sidewinder aboard with an automatic lockon, air-to-air radar mode selected. Flight instruments are below and immediately to the right of the video screen and engine instruments are to the far right.

What the F-16 does possess is its fire control radar which means, unlike other CAS types, the F-16 pilot receives vital information on enemy aircraft threats outside of air-to-air weapon employment ranges. With this airplane, loaded, the F-16 pilot still has the ability to go 550 knots (the general munitions restriction speed), the energy to pull and sustain a high 'G' load (the airplane can still pull 9 'Gs' but the weapons are generally limited to 5.5 'Gs') and AIM-9L Sidewinders, plus guns which it is hoped will neutralize the airborne threat and allow the mission to continue. The F-16's abilities would not be used to avoid a CAS mission and go air-to-air, but rather to fight its way in to support groundforces if possible. Naturally, following a strike and free of CAS ordnance, the F-16 comes back into its own as a premier dogfighter and can fight its way out against the best adversaries.

At typical F-16 speeds, it will spend much less time in enemy detection and acquisition areas. Its small size and high performance will help it avoid being hit and pilots point out that the F-16's speed provides the best protection and that the airplane is less susceptible to be hit than other, larger, slower, less agile aircraft. Midair collision data has shown that the F-16 is very capable of continued flight after major airframe damage. Its structure contains redundant structural load paths which means considerable damage can be sustained without major failure and the airplane becoming a statistic. By no stretch of the imagination is the F-16 as hit resistant as the A-10 but its chances of

getting hit are far less and most pilots would rather go with the F-16 under the circumstances.

In the Gulf War, the F-16's speed and agility was brought into play in the role of a "Fast-FAC". Operational improvements shortened the time lag from detecting targets to hitting them. F-16s were praised for greatly increasing effectiveness of strikes against Iraqi troops. Rather than using slower OA-10s, the fast F-16s brought target identification and strike time to a much shorter interval.

The one versus two engine controversy continues and is a valid consideration regarding a CAS F-16. Powerplant interruption of any sort in a single-engine aircraft usually has grave consequences and generally results in aircraft loss, or at least mission loss. As has been demonstrated, the F-16 can be guided to a successful deadstick landing. In a combat environment, at low altitude, this capability may not mean very much.

As pointed out, combat loss rates due to failure of a single powerplant falls to below 2 per cent with a twin-engine aircraft. At least three countries elected to purchase the F/A-18 Hornet in large measure because of the two-engine reliability factor. The other side of that coin is that statistics also show that a single-engine aircraft tends to be harder to hit than a dual-engine airplane due to smaller area.

General Dynamics elected to go with a single engine due to common usage with the F-15, less costs, a reduction in installed weight and a significant decrease in fuel consumption with increased range. In this argument, General Dynamics initially said the evidence was inconclusive then, in the face of considerable evidence to the contrary, declared there was really no difference in accidents or combat losses due to having a single engine. Any of the many pilots who have had a second engine get them out of harm's way will vociferously dispute such aberrant conclusions. The company most assuredly anticipated this argument and did studies to confirm that military aircraft accidents related to engine problems are decreasing.

A company Vice President and F-16 program manager said that of total accidents, 20 per cent are engine related. Of that 20 per cent, 12 per cent are caused by subsystem failure, 6 per cent FOD, and 2 per cent caused by the engine itself. While FOD vulnerability was reduced by nosegear placement, these factors relate to accidents *per se*, and not combat. And it is in combat where even the most reliable engine suffers under the onslaught of AAA. Certainly, the engine's reliability under peacetime operations has been exemplary. Combat is another matter. Acknowledging this hazard, the Air Force is considering use of possibly a Kevlar-based composite armor around the engine as well

as around hydraulic actuators and the cockpit. The fact remains, one minus one still equals zero and the F-16 is penalized by such basic mathematics.

The F-16 will receive a number of enhancements in the near future which will aid not only its multi-mission capability but also its CAS role in particular.

The currently named 'Falcon Eye' or a derivative is a pilot's head steered, forward-looking infra-red (FLIR) sensor which projects life-size or magnified infra-red imagery into the pilot's helmet eyepieces. With ATHS and a cockpit digital map display which would provide pilots with their location and surroundings, the Falcon Eye provides the F-16 pilot with enhanced situational awareness and the ability to fly CAS tactics at night.

Ordnance capability enhancements are already under way which could double the F-16's air-to-ground firepower. Known as Low-Cost-Advanced-Technology-Missiles (LOCATM), they would be housed in an Expendable Intelligent Multiple Ejector Rack

Above: The Syracuse 174th TFW Special Bavaria Crest insignias are only on one of the unit's F-16As, number 79-0403, the commander's airplane. On the A-10, the 'Bavaria' meant the aircraft had actually been to Germany on simulated NATO training exercises. The crests represent Bavarian Lion heraldry, and the patch of Fighter-Bomber Wing (FBW) 32, a Tornado unit based near Munich, a long-time sister unit to the 174th TFW.

Opposite: Colonel Thomas J. Costello, New York State ANG Deputy Commander For Operations, about to board his F-16A for a night refuelling mission. His career is enviable with some 1,600 hours in the F-86F and H models, 120 in the A-37, 650 in the F-100D, 150 in the A-7, nearly 1,000 in the A-10, and now over 200 in the F-16. His CAS expertise is second to none and, having flown all the CAS types, he feels the F-16 is the most capable aircraft available for the CAS/BAI mission.

(XIMER). This unit would offer less drag than normal exposed weapons and provide the F-16 with speed and range advantages. The munitions, up to six independently targeted weapons, would be nestled together in one streamlined and expendable unit. Of great advantage is the fact that once shot, these weapons are on their own guided by integral, on-board electronics. The pilot is then able to go on to new targets, to fight, or escape as required.

Is the F-16 truly a 'Jack of all trades', and good at them all? Under scrutiny, it turns out that General Dynamics gave us a product that can do air-to-air or CAS/BAI/attack a great deal better than anything else available, even considering performance per dollar. It has its faults as noted but its attributes are stunning.

The Low-Altitude Navigation and Targeting Infra-Red for Night (LANTIRN) system is a combination of navigation and targeting pods enabling the F-16 to use terrain following radar coupled with an infra-red sensor designed for target detection, lock-on and tracking plus laser designator and range-finder, and missile boresight correlator functions. The F-16 pilot will be able to operate at night at 200 feet above the ground (AGL) in all terrain.

No doubt, the F-16 will be around for a long time and General Dynamics even has plans to keep derivatives in production through the year 2005.

In the CAS role, the phenomenal agility of the F-16 coupled with the electronics as described should allow a successful entry to the target area, at least a one pass acquisition and attack with surgical accuracy, and successful exit. Considering the available alternatives as well as the political and economic environment of our time, the F-16 clearly is the most apt and viable answer.

Operation Desert Storm provided some insight into the F-16's immense capabilities in a hostile environment. The Falcon required only about 50% in dollar value in spares compared to an F-15. Further, it was reliable. One pilot reported that in 28 consecutive combat missions in 27 days, he had no late takeoffs and no ground or air aborts.

The final ingredient is the person in the cockpit and, as pilots who have flown all the CAS types proclaim, they would rather go to work in the F-16 than anything else.

Below: Colonel Costello at engine start. Note the large, clear, one-piece canopy which has no bow to obstruct vision. The HUD is directly in front of the pilot with a television/video sensor directly below. This particular F-16A, number 79-0335, is assigned to Major Joe Bulmer who flew number three position with the USAF Thunderbirds demonstration team, is now the Air Force Advisor to the Syracuse 174th TFW, and has over 1,000 hours in the F-16.

Opposite: The author's self-portrait during an afterburner maximum-rate climb out of Syracuse, New York. Note the runway environment directly below the aircraft as it accelerates vertically. Rate of climb in afterburner at low altitudes has been calculated at about 42,000 feet per minute! Maximum afterburner climb schedule for maximum time to climb performance is 575 knots to 0.90 Mach which is maintained until altitude. An F-16 maximum afterburner climb is eye-watering!

CONCLUSION

The emerging capabilities in navigation, communication and targeting are the answer to future CAS/BAI. Air-to-air capability is mandatory since we cannot choose whether or not to fight in the air — the enemy will make that decision for us.

The CAS pilot still experiences the same frustrations with which he fought in the Southeast Asian war including trying to co-ordinate targets with an airborne or ground-based FAC. What the new equipment and philosophies really do is attack the CAS *system* in order to provide responsive and accurate support. The notion that fast jets cannot do the job stems from past problems and frustrations without realizing the *real* source of the poor performance — and speed is really not the issue. The culprits are poor weapons delivery accuracy, poor co-ordination between ground and air and unreliable navigation aids. The new tech-nologies face those issues. An added benefit of the new systems is high-threat, night CAS capability — no more working under flares or with ground markers or diving into unknown dark holes!

A CAS optimized, F-16 is the only option that makes sense considering logistics, finance and performance.

In the short term, the F-16 will share the air-to-ground role with the A-10 but the A-10 inventory will be reduced as F/A-16 numbers increase. The Defense Department has decided to retrofit current F-16s for CAS rather than produce a new A-16. A Cost and Operational Effectiveness Analysis concluded that no other existing aircraft can truly match an upgraded F-16.

Opposite: Aircraft 79-0337, Callsign 'Cobra 21' on this mission, flown by Lt Colonel Denny Lombard, levels out *en route* to the low-altitude CAS training mission. His aircraft carries the 30mm gun pod and AIM-9L Sidewinders. Typical of high-quality aviators in the Syracuse F-16 unit, Denny has extensive experience first as an F-4 pilot with foreign duty at Kunsan AB, Korea, then as an A-10 Instructor Pilot at RAF Bentwaters, UK, and Syracuse ANG, New York, and now as an F-16 pilot with the 174th TFW.

Above: Looking down on Lt Colonel Lombard's aircraft, the F-16 pilot's exceptional visibility is obvious. Note the knee clipboard in use. Dark smudges around the 20mm gun port indicate the gun has been recently fired. Syracuse F-16s use the 'Cobra' callsign and their aircraft flaunt a cobra figure on the fuselage above the gunport.

Above: Proceeding to the training area, the F-16 flies over the beautiful early October landscape of upstate New York. Well-used fuselage access panels are prominently outlined.

Overleaf: Another author self-portrait illustrating the F-16 pilot's remarkable visibility, including rearwards. The F-16 on the wing reveals its extraordinary shape accentuated by huge underbody airscoop, sharp leading edge forebody strakes and long nose.

Opposite: Inverted, this F-16 clearly displays its GPU-5 30mm gun pod, weapons pylons and dorsal fins. These vertical fins enhance directional stability and are aluminum skinned over a bonded aluminum honeycomb core. Just below and behind the air intake scoop is a UHF blade antenna, an IFF/transponder antenna, plus another threat warning antenna (RHAW) cover.

Rolling away, the F-16 exhibits its unusual
forward fuselage-to-wing profile. Note the
retracted arrestor hook between the ventral
fins, a device used for emergency stopping.
Syracuse F-16 undersides are painted in FS
36375 — 'Light Gray', also known as 'Light
Ghost Gray'.

Above: The Falcon's sharp edged forebody strakes and wing blending are unmistakable in this view. Here, the Falcon insignia is carried on the fuselage just aft of the cockpit. On the fuselage spine, the air-refuelling receptacle slipway door area is well defined by 'Dark Gull Gray' — FS 36231, stripes and outline. Production F-16 topside colors are FS 36270 — 'Neutral Gray', and FS 36118 — 'Gunship Gray'. The radome is also FS 36270, but appears darker since the paint is applied over fiberglass material.

Opposite: Framed by the colorful Fall foliage of upstate New York, Cobra 21 uses full afterburner to illustrate acceleration from a slow 250 knots to 600 knots, a time frame of about 15 seconds. the F-16's clean aircraft maximum speeds are 800 knots from sea level to 30,000 feet then the limit is Mach 2.05.

Above: Joining up with another Syracuse F-16 flight. The leader is Captain Tom McChesney, a full-time F-16 pilot with the Syracuse ANG in 79-0335, and his wingman is Major John Reed in 79-0368. Major Reed has over 1,200 combat hours in Vietnam — as an Army Cobra pilot! Lt Colonel Lombard flies number three position in 79-0337.

Opposite: Turning for Syracuse, all these 174th TFW Block 10 F-16s carry the AIM-9L Sidewinder, the lead aircraft also carries empty TER-9A triple ejector racks, and 79-0337 has the GPU-5A 30mm gun pod.

Above: Lt Colonel Phil Hofmann sporting his Syracuse CAS patch takes on a 'Star Wars' image with dark helmet and visor. A graduate of the US Air Force Academy, Lt Colonel Hofmann went on to fly the F-4C, D and E models, then went to Southeast Asia as a 'Nail' OV-10 FAC at Nakhon Phanom, Thailand. He later flew the F-15 at Holloman AFB, New Mexico, and attended the Fighter Weapons School at Nellis AFB, Nevada, in the F-15 Eagle. He flew the A-10 as a CAS pilot for six years with the Syracuse ANG and now has three years in the F-16. He is the Operations Officer with the 138th TFS at Syracuse.

Opposite: In a descent towards Syracuse's Hancock Field, speed brakes are deployed and can be seen extended either side of the inboard horizontal tail surfaces. Another threat warning antenna (RHAW) is inside the fairing atop the vertical tail's trailing edge.

Above: Gear down, flaps down, on final approach to Hancock Field, Syracuse, New York. A normal, overhead approach is flown at 300 knots. After pitchout and below 300 knots, the gear is lowered. Approach speed is based on weight, on this particular load computing to about 145 knots with touchdown occurring around 135 knots.

Opposite: Two-point aerodynamic nose-high braking is used down to 80 knots when the nosewheel is flown onto the runway. Maximum effective two-point aerodynamic braking is achieved at thirteen degrees angle-of-attack (AOA). If fifteen degrees is exceeded, the engine exhaust nozzle, speedbrakes and ventral fins will contact the runway. That fine line is evident in this photo.

Above: A sunset silhouette illustrates the F-16's distinctive cantilevered forward fuselage. The nose area houses the APG-66 radar. While the nose area is quite small, Westinghouse managed to produce an excellent radar system that fits inside. The fiberglass radome houses the entire radar antenna assembly. The reclined position of the pilot's seat is also very clear.

Top: The Syracuse ANG patch has always had a yellow circle with some 'clever' slogan. With the F-86H it was 'Last of the Sports Models'. Its A-37s received 'The Smallest Fighter — The Fastest Gun: A-37' and its A-10 patch appropriately said 'Go Ugly Early: A-10'. While the current F-16 patch is controversial, it does express the fact that the Syracuse F-16 unit is the fastest CAS outfit around.

Opposite: An F-16 launches into the sunset in full afterburner, a visual and aural extravaganza. With an airframe designed for 8,000 hours, the F-16 should be around a long time.